THE GABRIELLI MAN

Claudia had hated Nicolo Gabrielli for a long time—the time it had taken her to recover from the accident he had been the cause of. Now she was out for revenge. . .

THE
GABRIELLI MAN

BY

JENETH MURREY

MILLS & BOON LIMITED
15–16 BROOK'S MEWS
LONDON W1A 1DR

First published in Great Britain 1984 by Mills & Boon Limited

© *Jeneth Murrey 1984*

Australian copyright 1984 Philippine copyright 1985 This edition 1985

ISBN 0 263 74954 1

Set in Monophoto Times 11 on 11 pt. 01–0285 – 53285

Made and printed in Great Britain by Richard Clay (The Chaucer Press) Ltd, Bungay, Suffolk

CHAPTER ONE

'YOU'RE doing *what?*' Judy Liss set the teapot down with a thump which jangled every teacup in its saucer. 'Claudia, you're out of your mind, you *must* be. After what you went through! And then to calmly sit there and tell me you're going back to Italy for a holiday, to the very same place. In your shoes, I'd rather opt for the North Pole.'

'But you're not in my shoes, are you?' Claudia raised a dark eyebrow and gave a careful little smile which didn't reach her hazel eyes. 'They wouldn't fit you—too big,' she took a bite at a sizeable hunk of jam sponge and chewed it reflectively. 'This isn't up to your usual standard, Judy; it's chewy.'

'My new mixer. . . .'

'Not as good as the old one?'

'Of course it is, it's better and quicker. I whipped the thing up in half the time but I forgot to put the oven on earlier so the tins were a bit cold going in and the mix didn't rise properly— Drat you, Claudia, you've changed the subject.'

'As I've every right to do,' Claudia pointed out gravely. 'Now it's up to you to talk about something else. Show a little delicacy.'

'I won't,' Judy was cheerfully obstinate. 'I'm not delicate, I'm like a bull in a china shop—always have been—it's part of my charm.'

'It's part of your custom,' Claudia corrected. 'This habit you have of crashing in where angels would fear to tread, specially when you've seen the notice, "Keep Out"!'

'It's the old lure of the forbidden,' Judy grinned and her plain face crinkled charmingly, 'and I won't be put off by any old notice. You're going for a holiday to the very place which'll bring back all those old, sad memories, you're going to stay again in Maris' villa. . . .'

'Not again,' Claudia shook her head. 'I've never stayed there, we didn't get that far, if you remember and it's not Maris' villa any longer, it's mine now.'

'Oh yes, now that, I *do* remember. Maris left it to you together with all her other worldly goods.'

Claudia sighed with exasperation. 'I wish you'd get your facts straight instead of making sweeping statements. Maris didn't *leave* me anything. I just collected because I was her only relation. There was this villa on the coast—you can see Elba from the *salotto* windows—her flat in Rome, the boutique and her workshop. I sold the last two, I'm a painter not a designer but I kept the villa and the apartment although I've never visited either of them—Now, I think I should. I feel like a holiday after the gruelling three months I've just spent in that cosmetic surgery clinic and I never saw a bit of Rome because the six months I was there, I was in hospital.'

'You were lucky to be alive; in fact, according to the papers, it was you that was killed,' Judy plunged into the forbidden ground with both feet. 'You and James—a mix up over the names, they said afterwards. A damn fool thing to do, calling two girls in the same family by the same name— the sort of thing that's bound to lead to confusion.'

'Blame our fathers,' Claudia held out her cup for more tea. 'Identical twins do things like that. I remember Gran telling me that she always had to take both of them, my father and Maris', to the dentist because only he could tell which of them had real toothache and which was only suffering in sympathy. It would have been worse if Mummy hadn't changed mine round to Claudia Maris.'

'So that's how the papers got it wrong.'

'Mmm,' Claudia stirred in a heaped spoonful of sugar and then added another. 'I hadn't had time to get my passport changed before the wedding and when we got to Pisa where Maris was meeting us—James,' she congratulated herself silently—she'd said that name twice without allowing a flicker of pain to cross her face, 'James,' she repeated it, 'tucked our marriage certificate into his wallet with *his* passport and the details on it matched Maris' passport well enough for the paparazzi to end up with the wrong story.'

Claudia was doing more than congratulating herself, she was surprising herself. Sitting in this cosy room and talking about something as though it had happened to somebody else, as though her life hadn't ended when James' had and she was once more a real human being instead of an empty shell which walked, talked, ate, drank, slept and wakened by rote and not inclination. Since she'd gone this far, surely she could go a bit further.

'It all added up for the gossip writers,' her throat was making noises and her lips were framing the words, that was all. There wasn't any meaning to the words, she was talking like a well-rehearsed parrot. 'Two people dead in a car, a marriage certificate and the woman had the right name, more or less—therefore they were man and wife and it made a good story with Maris being so well known in Rome. Front page, no less. Nobody even bothered to look for another woman, not until the day after; and when they found me, I couldn't tell them anything, so they were quite satisfied with their little fiction. A car with two people in it went over a cliff during the worst storm of the year—end of story!'

'There!' Judy sounded satisfied. 'You've said it! D'you feel better now?'

'Surprisingly, I do,' Claudia admitted and knew she was telling the truth. She hadn't told the whole story, there'd been a lot more to it than that— she'd left out Maris' tale—but in telling her own small part of it, she'd seemed to purge herself of some of the pain. Perhaps it might even help her constantly recurring nightmares—she had sleeping pills but on the one occasion that she'd taken them, she'd felt much worse than if she'd lived through the nightmare again. Besides, her dreams weren't quite so vivid nowadays, the sharp lines were smudging like a much-handled charcoal sketch and sometimes things happened in the dream which were out of sequence with the reality she'd lived through. These nights she hardly ever felt herself being flung out of the car before it went over the edge of the cliff to fall on to the rocks below that part had vanished so, maybe in time, all the other things which haunted her would vanish as well.

She uncurled her legs from where she was sitting on them and, stretching them out, wiggled her toes to get the blood flowing once more. 'What do you think of my new face, Judy? Would you call it an improvement?'

With a finger her chin, turning the said face this way and that, Judy exaggerated the inspection and then shook her head. 'Doesn't look much different to me,' she gave her considered opinion. 'Maybe a bit thinner and that bump you had on your nose has gone but apart from that. ... It's your hair, I think. That's what had me fooled the first time I saw you.'

Claudia lifted a hand and ran her fingers through her short, crisp, silver blonde curls; remembering what it had been like before—a heavy fall of leaf brown hair which waved down to her shoulders and which, when the sun caught it, glowed with the tint of autumn.

'But more convenient, don't you think?' She made a wry grimace, 'I shan't ever have to touch up the colour when the time comes—I'm white already, but my face—the scars don't show now, do they?' She heard herself sounding anxious.

'Not a trace, they've done a marvellous job and, as I said before, they've improved your nose. Remember how Roman it used to be and how we used to call you "Hookey" like the Duke of Wellington? As a matter of fact, you look a bit more like Maris than you used to do.' Judy paused as though she was hesitating about saying all she thought and then her mouth firmed and she jumped in as usual with both feet.

'Your eyes are the worst, they're like windows with the blinds drawn. Like there were no feelings behind them.'

'My feelings, as you call them, died in hospital,' Claudia snorted. 'And also during the three months when I was done up like the Man in the Iron Mask and they fed me through a slit in the bandaging but, if you'll give your blessing to my holiday in Italy, I'll promise to grow a brand new set for you.'

'Bring me back one of your landscapes,' Judy

bargained. 'An original, a "one off". I've never been able to afford better than a reproduction and I'd love to be able to boast about having a genuine Claudia Currey. Only a little one of course, I don't expect you to waste your time on something enormous if it's only for me.'

'It will be gigantic, that's if I haven't lost my touch,' Claudia promised. 'It's what I owe you, in fact I owe you so much more. Taking me in when I was discharged from the clinic—when I had nowhere else to go. . . . Putting up with my moods. . . .'

'Shut up!' Judy was inelegant. 'You've paid your way and we've loved having you. Shall we see about starting dinner or do you think it's too early?'

Claudia pushed her feet into her slippers and stood up to straighten her rumpled skirt, she felt an air of purpose about herself, as if the road she'd decided on was opening up in front of her, but she wasn't going to say anything to anybody about that. The road would be fraught with difficulties and at the end of it was something which was better kept hidden.

Revenge was a nasty word but it was what she was living for—what she'd been living for ever since they'd told her, in the hospital in Rome, that James was dead. Everybody, nurses, doctors and even Signor Marinotta, Maris' lawyer, had been surprised at how swiftly she'd regained her health and strength. The doctors and nurses in the clinic, too—they'd praised her for never complaining while they'd flayed her back to get the skin to patch her face.

And it was all because she was viciously, evilly intent on vengeance. James, her husband, had been taken from her before he'd been a husband, before she'd been a wife—she knew who was to blame for that and she was going to exact payment. The person responsible was going to suffer, she was determined on it!

'I'll start on the potatoes, Judy,' she said serenely. 'I'll leave the meat to you, you're a better cook than I am.' And she went off to the kitchen, looking as though butter wouldn't melt in her mouth.

Claudia jammed her brush back into the jar of turps, leaned back on her little, collapsible canvas stool and, closing one eye, she looked at the results of her day's work. Damn! She'd done it again for the third time—painted not what she saw but what she felt and for Judy, it just wouldn't do. Judy wanted something which would make her feel good and this canvas wouldn't do that. On the surface, it was pretty—pretty enough, a casually bright scene, the focal point of which was the huge, rambling villa which sprawled on a hill.

Look at it once and it was just that, a villa, shining white walls, red pantiled roofs rising above the grey green of olive trees and the taller, darker spires of cypress. But Judy wasn't going to look at it 'just once'. She was going to see it day after day, every time she walked into her lounge and Judy had a nose for atmosphere—it wouldn't take her long to see this canvas was loaded with it.

Claudia tipped back her wide-brimmed straw hat—the doctors at the clinic had advised against a lot of sun on her so recently repaired face. They said she'd go patchy as the three small skin grafts which covered the worst of her scarring wouldn't tan evenly with the rest of her face. She would have a white patch above one eyebrow, another on her cheekbone and the third would stand out on her chin—hence, the hat. And she tried to decide what she'd done wrong. Unconsciously she must have darkened the blue of the sky behind the villa to a dull pewter and added a tinge of purple to the red tiles of the roofs—which would account for the odd air of menace about the beautiful building— and the cypresses, she hadn't painted them straight and tall but had bent each slender tip as if it was being stirred by a strong wind.

Perhaps she ought to get it out of her system, paint not what she saw but what she felt and then, maybe, on the next try, she'd be able to get the chocolate box, the picture-postcard view which Judy would like. Instead of reaching for her turps-soaked rag, she grabbed for the brush, loaded it with paint and began to darken the sky even further.

Unthinkingly, she worked on, hardly looking at what she was doing, whitening the already white walls, deepening the shadows on them while she tried to occupy her mind with sane, safe thoughts. The journey here had been quite relaxing—she'd taken four days to do it, never travelling more than two hundred miles a day, sometimes less, but that was because of the car, a very used model which she'd bought quite cheaply.

She recalled the salesman, young and eager, who had equated her with a second-hand, hardly used Lotus Elan and the way he had looked startled when she had shuddered away from it and marched across to the very mundane Allegro in chocolate brown with a narrow gold trim. The poor fellow was thinking in terms of commission, he wasn't to know that she shuddered away from any white sports car—in her dreams and night-mares, that was part of the horror, the white car skidding, rolling across the road and toppling over the edge out of sight so that she could only hear the noise as it bumped and crashed its way to the rocks below and she, lying helpless, unable even to call for help or move and the bronze of her dress blending so well with the wet ditch she was lying in. Several cars had passed, she'd heard the kiss of their tyres on the wet surface but nobody had stopped.

Savagely she went on deepening shadows, making walls look thicker and windows deeper set, emphasising the wrought iron balconies until they looked more like twisted and distorted prison bars. And then there had been Judy's tearful farewell.

'Mind you take care of yourself,' she'd said. 'Although how you've the courage to get into a car again after the experience you've had, I don't know.'

Claudia hadn't known either but she hadn't said so. She'd laughed instead and promised postcards from every stop on the way, while inside she felt as though she was bleeding to death.

'It's us quiet ones who surprise everybody,' she'd bantered. 'Everybody thinks we're deep and thoughtful but we're not. We're shallow and without a thought in our heads. We've no imagination, we're like cows in a field, lumbering from one tuft of grass to another and giving the occasional moo to relieve the monotony.' She'd managed to divert Judy by looking at her one, rather battered suitcase which was visibly bulging.

'I wonder if I can get any more in that? I've just remembered, I haven't packed my palette and I could do with some spare canvases. I've a few already stretched but they take up so much room....'

And Judy, tears forgotten, had raced away to find another case. It had been a low down trick to play on so good a friend as Judy but needs must when the devil drives and the devil on her back was driving hard!

Reluctantly, she dragged her attention back to her work, trying to see it with an unprejudiced eye—She hadn't altered much, not really. The villa looked a bit older and not as well cared for, that was all she'd achieved. None of her huge hate had come through so it wasn't the villa she was hating—but she knew that already. The villa was only a prop, the wings and backcloth to tragedy. With a sigh, she threw down the brush and reached for a rag to wipe off the wet paint.

'No, signora. Don't erase it!'

The voice was like dark brown velvet—the last time she'd heard it, it hadn't been like that. It had been nearly two years ago and then it had been hard—steely with an ice-cold cutting edge. It had spoken in Italian—she had no gift for languages so she hadn't understood more than one word in every hundred, often not that but she hadn't needed to understand the words, the meaning had been quite clear.

Maris, wet through and with her face looking like a Greek tragic mask had been begging—Maris begging! She'd never thought to hear her arrogant, volatile cousin beg, would never have believed it possible that Maris could do such a thing, but she had—her face completely white in the lamplight over the door so that her eyes looked like two huge dark holes and the deep plum of her lipstick writhing as she'd poured out her plea. And what had she got for it? A spate of Italian which had lasted nearly a minute but which could have been reduced to two English words—'Get lost!'

Without turning her head, Claudia reached for the brush she'd thrown down, wiped it on the rag, dabbled it about in the mug of turps, wiped it again and laid it carefully back in the box.

Unlike Alice, she couldn't curtsey while she was thinking what to say but she could keep her hands occupied, if only to disguise the fact that they were shaking. But whether it was with excitement or triumph or just plain fear, she didn't know.

The brush laid down meticulously in its place, she lifted the canvas from the portable easel, held it in one hand while she pulled down the brim of her straw hat with the other and turned to face the man.

'In that case, perhaps you would care to have it, signor,' she extended the painting so that it was almost a barrier between them. 'It's no good to me, it hasn't the effect I was aiming for but it's still wet so be careful. Oil paints don't come off clothes easily.'

Long slim hands accepted it gracefully. '*Tante grazie*, signora. You are now fully recovered, I hope?'

Claudia lowered her head even further so that only the top of her hat and the wide brim were visible above her shoulders. So much for her hope that she looked different—Judy had told her it wasn't so, that the only things changed were her nose and her hair, neither of which were visible but she'd been pig-headed, certain that she'd go unrecognised, too certain but, as she'd thought, with good reason.

He'd only seen her the once and not under very

good conditions. One overhead light had shone down on the group—Maris, this man and herself. James had stayed in the car, but he'd have come if she'd needed him. The night had been one of storm, lightning forking across the sky and a raging wind blowing rain so that the drops stung her bare face and she hadn't been looking her best. Her dress had been stained with rain, her face had been hollow with tiredness and hunger and her hair had escaped from its pins to hang in a sodden mass around her face and shoulders, but he'd looked at her, a long, considering look before he'd spoken to Maris so ruthlessly.

For a moment, Claudia's vision was obscured by a red mist of furious hating anger and she had to blink several times before she could see normally again. She raised her head until she could look into his face. Lord, she'd never forget that face!

The skin drawn tightly over aquiline features, the bold, hawklike nose; the almond shaped eyes; heavy lidded and fringed with long black lashes, set slightly aslant under black straight brows; and the hair, guinea gold behind his ears but fairer where the sun had bleached it as it curled back from his wide, high forehead. Not a typical Italian face, too many angles and the colouring was wrong. For her, slanting, dark brown eyes and fair hair spelled Venetian.

Given a clean sheet of paper and a piece of charcoal, she could reproduce that face, every line of it. She'd done so, over and over again, so many times that her waste basket had been full of crumpled, discarded cartoons—each one looking like the devil incarnate. With a sigh, she pushed the past away to concentrate on the present. With this man, she couldn't afford to be anything but ultra careful.

'Yes, thank you, signor, I'm completely recovered,' she murmured it in her new voice—something to do with the work the surgeons had done on her nose, they'd warned her about that—and she kept it quietly husky and colourless while her face remained almost expressionless but inside, she was raw and bleeding.

'On the outside, yes. I agree you seem to be quite recovered,' he nodded as if he was graciously agreeing with her. 'But inside, I think that might be a different story. You still grieve for your young husband?'

Judy had once asked her very much the same question only it had been girl talk and a lot more earthy. 'Do you miss him, I mean in bed?'

'We didn't,' she answered. 'There wasn't time.'

'But before, when you were engaged,' Judy was very modern. 'These days, most couples do. . . .' and Claudia had cut her off with a curt 'We didn't and as Gran always said, what you never had, you never miss!' But it wasn't Judy asking the question now and girl talk wouldn't do. She phrased it more obliquely.

'I'm learning to live with it and,' a mad impulse made her raise the straw hat from her head, 'I *am* slightly changed, as you can see.'

'Mmm,' he nodded again, this time without a trace of sympathy. 'I admired your hair, it was such a rich colour but this,' he indicated her short, silvery curls with a flick of his fingers, 'this is also very becoming. And now,' he held the painting with one hand while, with the other he investigated the contents of her lunch box, shaking his head at the meagre packet. 'Come up to the villa with me, please, and share my lunch. A piece of cheese and an apple is hardly sufficient for a young woman who is still convalescent.'

'It's all I need.'

'I disagree,' he was quite firm as he reached past her to replace the painting on the easel, stepping back a pace to examine it and letting his arm drop across her shoulder. She flinched from his touch but pride kept her still. 'You need food, proper food. Don't you know the whole village is worried to death about you?'

'Worried about me?' Claudia snorted her disbelief, 'I'm surprised to learn anybody knows I'm here.' She was wanting desperately to get away from him but her vengeance was keeping her by his side. Whenever she'd thought about it, which was never less than once a day, she'd only ever been able to plan as far as being in the same bit of territory which he occupied. What she would or should do then had been a mystery but she had convinced herself that she'd think of something. She'd achieved that first part, but now caution was telling her to get the hell out of it, while revenge was pointing out—quite sensibly—that you couldn't hurt a man unless you knew how and where to hurt and something like that took time to discover, so she played for time, listening to his quiet answer which was more of a reprimand.

'Everybody in the village knows you are here, signora. They've even given you a pet name. To them, you're Monna Inglese, a rather old-fashioned title, not in use nowadays but these are old-fashioned people. Maria, who maids the Villa Cristal for you, she worries that you don't eat and when Maria worries all our little world has to worry with her. She has even brought you food, thinking perhaps that you might be as poor as she is herself, but you haven't eaten her offerings.'

A puzzle had been explained and she almost crowed with laughter as she realised the why and wherefore of the small dishes of lasagna and other sorts of pasta which had appeared mysteriously in her fridge and, the next day, had disappeared just as mysteriously.

'I thought it was her lunch which she had brought with her. I'm out most of the day, you see. Oh dear, I hope I haven't offended her, I wouldn't like to do that, she's such a nice person. I suppose it's my fault, the language barrier, you know. I don't seem to be able to learn foreign languages.'

'It's easy! But it is your appetite we are talking about. So, I'll repeat my invitation. Signora, will you share my lunch with me? And you'll say "*Molte grazie*, signor" and we'll go. The car is waiting on the road at the bottom of this little hill.'

Claudia clapped her hat back on her head, and beneath the wide brim her eyes gleamed with something like triumph. He was making it so easy for her. She had thought she'd have to scrape an acquaintance with him but now the road ahead was straight and clear. She could turn aside if she wished or she could go where it led.

'*Molte grazie*, signor,' she parroted and set her foot on the first step along the road she'd chosen.

He offered an arm as they went down the long, grassy slope to the car but she pretended not to notice, as she pretended not to notice the hand which he offered beneath her elbow to help her into the car—a largish black one, she would have refused to enter it had it been white. She slid into

the passenger seat without help and settled herself
back against the leather upholstery, thinking that
the really bad part was to come. It would be the
moment when she had to force herself to enter the
house with him, to go past the place where Maris
had pleaded with him.

The thought robbed her face of any little colour
it might have had but she knew it would have to
be done and she screwed herself up to do it until
she could feel herself going rigid, her hands
clenched so tightly that her nails bit into her
palms.

'I forgot, signora,' he put the car in motion, the
wheels churning up a fine cloud of dust on the
unmade surface of the road. 'I haven't introduced
myself so, while I know your name, you don't
know mine.'

But she did! She made a great effort to appear
quite normal—she had the feeling that she hadn't
been behaving normally for quite some time, that
she'd allowed herself to be almost too single
minded about her aims as far as he was concerned.
This man was no fool and she would have to be
careful, she had so much to hide and he mustn't be
allowed to see how she felt about him, that sort of
thing could ruin any chance she might have of
being revenged for her loss.

'Oh, but I *do* know your name, signor,' her lips
curved into a smile and she was glad of the wide-
brimmed hat which hid her eyes. There was no
smile in them! 'Everybody in the village knows
your name,' she continued brightly. 'I've heard it
mentioned frequently, with varying degrees of
reverence, of course. Signor Gabrielli, Signor
Nicolo Gabrielli, aren't I right?'

'Quite right.' She caught the flash of white teeth

as his stern, rather serious mouth parted in a smile which grooved two lines from his nose to the corners of his lips and made little wrinkles around his dark, oblique eyes.

Let him smile, she told herself. One day, she'd wipe that smile from his face forever. In her book, Nicolo Gabrielli was no better than a murderer. It was he who'd put Maris in such a state that she could no longer control the car in an emergency so, in effect, he was to blame for the accident which had killed James. He couldn't be more to blame if he'd pushed the car over the cliff with his own hands!

CHAPTER TWO

IN the bright sunlight of midday, the driveway up to the villa held no memories, no terrors for Claudia. The cypress trees which flanked it on either side were motionless in the still air and their dark foliage made them seem aloof. She breathed a sigh of relief when he drove past the steps which led up to the main door and, instead, continued along by the side of a terrace to stop where there was a break in the balustrading and three or four narrow steps led up from the drive.

As she got out of the car Claudia caught a flash of moving white, but it was so fast it was gone before she could make it out. Nicolo Gabrielli saw the turn of her head as she tried to follow the movement.

'Emilia, the housekeeper,' he explained. 'She likes to pretend she knows everything. Actually, she's probably seen us from a window and rushed out to lay another place so that her reputation won't suffer and she will be able to smile mysteriously when a little maid whispers that "Emilia *knew* the signor was bringing a guest to lunch!" We humour her whenever we can, she's quite old and a splendid cook.' He raised an eyebrow as she didn't respond. 'Now what are you looking harassed about?'

'My gear,' Claudia stood undecided, the table lured and so did the smell of food but she hesitated, a slight frown wrinkling her brows. 'Eat my salt, sing my song', that had been another one

of her gran's interminable sayings—there had
seemed to be one for any and every occasion. And
she knew that she didn't want to sing this man's
song, although, deprived of its apple and piece of
cheese, her stomach was demanding she should eat
his salt.

'My painting gear,' she explained. 'I left it up on
the hill. . . .'

'And it will still be there when I take you back,'
he assured her.

'Oh yes, I know that.' She flapped a hand to
show she wasn't disputing him. 'But my painting. . . .'

'*My* painting, signora,' he corrected. 'Remember, you said I might have it. . . .'

'That's just the point,' Claudia was becoming
nervously agitated and it showed in her voice,
which rose a little and started to wobble. 'It won't
be anybody's painting soon. You put it back on
the easel and we walked away and left it there. The
sun's too hot, it'll dry the paint too fast and the
thing will crack and flake. I meant to cover it with
a cloth, like I usually do. I—I ought really to go
back. . . .'

'First, you will eat some lunch, Claudia; I may
call you Claudia, may I not?' and without waiting
for a yea or nay, he continued smoothly, 'If the
conditions are as bad as you say, the damage is
already done, which is a pity because I liked it.'

'You liked it?' She paused, her mouth part open
and her eyes wide with surprise. 'But you couldn't!
I spoiled it. I over-painted parts of it so that it
didn't look so—so. . . .' Her voice petered out as a
hand in the middle of her back impelled her
towards a small door.

'Go and wash the turps from your fingers, it'll

spoil the taste of your food,' he instructed, as if she was a small child. 'Take off your smock as well,' his nose twitched. 'That also smells of paint.'

'And you prefer your guests to smell of Chanel No. 5?'

'Only the females.' She thought he sounded amused. 'I don't think a perfume like that would suit most men.'

It was a perfectly ordinary little washroom, no terrors lurked in the corners and Claudia scrubbed her hands and washed her face with cold water from the solitary tap. After she'd dried them on a rough towel she examined herself in the mirror over the basin. There were a few paint smears on her jeans but apart from that she was quite presentable. Her hair was too short to be untidy and she rammed the hat back on her head and pulled the brim well down while she considered the situation.

Nicolo Gabrielli was being friendly in a very pleasant, disarming way—probably the way he'd started his conquest of Maris—the lecher! Thoughtful consideration and a little praise to make a woman feel good—and it would have worked with Maris who'd had to fight every inch of the way through the world of fashion to reach the top and wasn't used to being treated as something delicate. Maris had grown a hard shell but it was only a shell. Underneath, she'd been looking for love which would have made her a pushover for the Gabrielli approach.

Yes, Claudia decided, she'd been quite right about her need to know him better—if she hadn't had Maris' example before her eyes, she might have softened towards him herself—but she *had* known and now she needed to know more—and she went out on to the terrace, unconsciously humming 'Getting to Know You' from *The King and I.*

'A good idea,' the Gabrielli man was smiling at her across the table as she took her seat. 'I think we should get to know each other better but first, food. The meat is chicken and Emilia has prepared an English salad for you. The wine is only medium dry, I think you'll like it and we'll talk over coffee. Do you have to keep that hat on all the time? I dislike talking to the top of it.'

'It's a habit when I'm painting,' she said it factually and wondered why she hadn't gone into a harrowing description of the work the surgeons had done on her face and how, for a while, much as she would love to feel the sun and wind on her face, she had to deprive herself of that simple pleasure. Why hadn't she made that bid for sympathy? A silly question and one she knew better than to ask herself. For a very simple reason, of course—the Gabrielli man wouldn't offer sympathy. She thought she must be getting his measure—he would probably nod understandingly and then point out with devastating logic that they were sitting in the shade!

She must have eaten enough to please Emilia for the old woman's face, brown and crinkled like a walnut, broke into smile and she pattered away with the near-empty dish of chicken and produced a dish of gelato like a conjuror getting a rabbit out of a hat, before she put a tray of coffee on a low table at the edge of the terrace and nudged two comfortable chairs towards it while the Gabrielli man escorted her across to it—tenderly and with a careful hand beneath her elbow, as though she wasn't capable of taking the four or five paces by herself, but she didn't shrug away from him although she wanted to. This was all part of the act and she would let it go on for a lot longer before she let the curtain down.

'And now we're comfortable,' he busied himself lighting a long, thin cheroot, 'we can talk. You said you'd spoiled your painting but I don't think so. You merely stripped away the romanticism and you must admit, the villa's a very romantic sight. From a distance, one gets the impression that all is as it was back in the days when the place was a palace, that was in the days when the Gabriellis were a rich and powerful family, counting soldiers, diplomats and a prince of the Church among their children. They built this place as an escape from the heat and dust of Sienna and they called it their Summer Palace and that's how the tourists are encouraged to see it—from a distance where its scars don't show.'

'And you think I showed the scars?'

'I think you showed the dignity of age, the once-smooth face now wrinkled, the sag in the line which was built so straight—which is as it should be. Youth and great age both have their different beauty.'

'A philosopher,' she derided, 'and all because I retouched a picture. Maybe I just wasn't satisfied with it. Remember, it was my work, the way I saw it. You can read into it what you like but I'm responsible for the actual presentation.'

'And I'm responsible for you,' he said it mildly, 'and therefore, in a way, responsible for what you do.'

This brought her head up with a jerk so that the wide-brimmed hat no longer concealed her face. 'I beg your pardon, signor, but I'm my own keeper—nobody is responsible for me or for what I do except myself.'

'Among certain, so called savage tribes'—his voice was quite beautiful when he spoke in this reflective way—'there's a belief that if one saves a person's life, then one doesn't exactly own that life but is responsible for it and for what happens to it. That's why I say I'm responsible for you.'

'*You* saved my life?' She laughed. 'Please tell me when, signor, I must have been very young at the time because I don't recall you doing any such thing.'

'No, I don't suppose you would remember, you were far too ill . . .'

'. . . and now, I'm consumed with curiosity.'

The heavy lids drooped over his dark brown, oblique eyes for a second before he lifted them and looked at her, holding her gaze. 'The evening after the accident, I heard the report of it on the radio. How a car had gone over the cliff during the storm and that the two occupants had both been killed instantly. I rang the carabiniere but they seemed quite satisfied—a man and a woman, they said and they described the car, but refused me the names. I think I must have been the only person who knew there were three people in that car, not two, and even I couldn't be sure. White sports cars are two a penny, as you say and it need not have been the one which I saw that night, so I made my own search and at last, I found you. I don't think you'd have survived another night in that ditch. As it was, your condition was critical.'

Claudia shrugged. 'So you saved my life, signor. I suppose I should be grateful, I suppose I am but I absolve you from any responsibility in the future. I don't need a guardian angel.'

Especially a dark angel, she added to herself and that's what he looked like with his sunbleached golden hair and dark, slanting eyes. Maris' dark angel who'd sent her and James to their deaths, leaving her, Claudia, alone, a widow before she'd ever been a wife.

'Such a grudging gratitude,' he murmured, 'and after all I did for you—the nights I spent beside your bed in the small hospital nearby—nights when I had to hold you because you tried to injure yourself. And when it was decided to move you to a hospital in Rome, you fought against being put in the ambulance and I had to be sent for again. The sisters couldn't cope with you.'

'Probably because it was a white ambulance?' A faint memory stirred but it was so hazy she couldn't decide whether it was actual memory or merely imagination. 'I still have a hatred of white cars.'

'So we discovered,' he gave a soft chuckle. 'You only calmed down when I carried you to that one,' he gestured in the direction of the car parked by the steps, 'and a most uncomfortable journey it was. You're no lightweight, Claudia, especially after nearly two hundred kilometres of being driven by one of the sisters at a very sedate pace. It seems you objected to anything white, even her coif.'

Maris had been wearing white that night, a stark white, simple linen shift and at the end, when they'd driven away—Maris had refused to allow James to drive her car and James, embarrassed by the scenes, had refused to sit in the front, saying Claudia could cope better than he—then Maris' face had been as white as her frock—white and dead looking.

'It seems I owe.' Claudia said it grimly. She

didn't relish the thought, but on analysis she still felt justified. Maybe he'd saved one life but he'd taken two, so she'd said no more than the truth. She *did* owe, or rather Nicolo Gabrielli owed, and she would make sure he payed. All she had to do was find out what was most precious to him and smash it to smithereens—ruin his life. She almost smacked her lips in anticipation of the day when she'd do just that. So, he'd saved her life, had he? One day he was going to rue that good deed—wish he'd left her lying there—passed by on the other side.

At this point, she caught herself up—being sadistically vengeful without allowing any of the outward signs to show was hard work. The suppression of her perfectly natural reactions was making her overly dramatic and she despised drama.

'Thank you for explaining,' she made her voice small and colourless. 'I seem to have been a great deal of trouble to you.'

'A little, certainly but,' once more the dark brown eyes held hers, 'women tend to bring trouble in their wake although, in your case, I think it was worth it. You and I are going to be friends, Claudia. No,' he held up a slender brown hand as she opened her mouth to speak. 'Don't say anything now—think about it first. You went through a very bad time two years ago but you were young and you should be getting over it by now. You're, let me see, twenty-five, isn't it? Young enough to adjust and to realise that life isn't an empty desert because you've lost your loved ones.'

'But it is, *it is*!' she wanted to scream it at him, but caution kept her silent. Without any effort on her part, she'd made a considerable amount of progress today—she'd accomplished within the space of a couple of hours more than she'd ever hoped for—and he'd said they were going to be friends. She would be able to get in close and put a finger on his weak spot.

'It's been a bad time,' she admitted gravely, 'and I'm having to adjust; not the easiest thing to do under the circumstances.' She gave him a quirky little smile which tipped up only one side of her mouth. 'The mornings are the worst when I'm still half asleep and I stumble to the bathroom and see an almost stranger in the mirror. Very off-putting.' She glanced at her watch and raised an eyebrow. 'You said you'd take me back, isn't it about time we were going. I don't want to take up too much of your time.'

'But it's at your disposal, Claudia. Now tell me, are you happy at the Villa Cristal?'

Claudia chuckled as they walked together down the steps to the car. 'When I can get used to the "open plan" thing, I will be. The bedrooms are all right, the doors can be secured from the inside, but there's no way of locking up the upper floor where the kitchen and lounge are. And there's that outside staircase—anybody could come up. But apart from that, it's a very nice place to live—easy to keep tidy and clean and the garden's out of this world. . . .'

The painting, saved by the shade of a small tree, didn't look as though it had suffered too much. The shadow had fallen across it as the sun rose to its zenith and the paint on the canvas felt cool and quite moist to her touch as she removed it from the easel and laid it aside. She made no attempt to pack up the rest of her stuff.

'You're not going back to the villa?' Nicolo's brows drew together in a frown. 'The hottest part of the day. . . .'

'No, of course not,' she gave him what she hoped was a dazzling smile as she rooted in her wooden case for a box of pastels and a pad of dark-coloured paper. 'I've a young man coming for a sitting at,' she glanced at her watch, 'any moment now so, if you'll excuse me. . . .' She gave him another smile, this time a rather absent one which was intended to dismiss him, only it didn't seem to have the right effect. He remained standing there, as if he'd taken root, very dark brown eyes making a comprehensive survey of her which brought a soft colour to her cheeks.

Knowing what the effect would be, she tugged at the hat brim until it nearly covered her face, only to have him gently push it up again, and his finger tip touched at the small white patches over her eyebrow, on her cheek and chin.

'It hardly shows, *cara*,' the finger tip drifted and touched her lips, 'and I'm glad you didn't hurt your mouth, it's a very lovely one; soft, warm and passionate. I wonder if it tastes like honey.'

'Vinegar,' she corrected tartly—things were moving a little too fast for her and she excused herself the little tremor of what could have been excitement. The Gabrielli man was really out of her class—he was a bit overpowering and besides, she hadn't rehearsed this far into the part she was playing yet—on second thoughts, she never dared allow herself to think it might be as easy as this. When he'd gone, taking the slope of the hill in long, free strides, she sat down on the stool with a sigh of relief.

She would have to be very careful—those dark,

slanting eyes saw too much—a cool, rather brittle approach would be best. He was wrong about the 'passionate' bit though, getting her muddled up with Maris. It was one thing James had always been pleased about—her detachment, her ability to think rather than feel. James had been wary of emotionalism, his love for her had been undemonstrative but none the worse for that, she told herself defiantly—at least, he hadn't pawed her about within a few hours of meeting her!

She banished her frown as a black, curly head came bobbing up the hill and resolved itself into Pietro, Maria's seven-year-old grandson who was carrying his most treasured possession—a straw sombrero with a conical crown and a truly magnificent brim, a gift from a camper on one of the nearby sites. The crown of the sombrero contained a small, sad-looking, liver-and-white puppy which lost its sadness when it was put down on terra firma and Pietro, with a grin which contained an angelic look together with all the wickedness in the world, took up his pose.

Claudia dropped her shopping on the kitchen counter, took a swift glance through the window to make sure the Allegro was safely tucked away out of sight and set about the preparations for her evening meal. Lettuce, tomatoes and some very thinly sliced ham which she assembled together on a tray, together with a newly purchased bottle of white wine. As an afterthought, she added a nectarine and carried the tray through to the lounge to set it on a small table on the terrace overlooking the garden.

From here, the view was splendid—she couldn't see the Villa Gabrielli. It had been four days since she'd lunched with the Gabrielli man and she'd seen neither hide nor hair of him since. So much for her self-congratulation! It was now evident to her that she'd built too high hopes on just one meeting but, her mouth curved in a wry little smile, she ought to have known it wouldn't be that easy or that quick and it wasn't as though she was short of time—she had the rest of her life if need be.

She ate part of her meal before abandoning it to leaf through her folder of pastel sketches—a commission for a company which produced calendars. Pietro would do very well for March or April, Maria for October and the one she'd done from memory of Emilia would make a good November. All she had to do was find other faces in the right age bracket for the other months of the year—perhaps Pietro's mother for July—a still beautiful woman, richly ripe although a bit overblown. She flicked through more pastel sketches of heads until she stiffened, almost like a hound on the scent.

Somewhere, in a book of war memoirs, read so long ago that she'd forgotten the author's name—forgotten even the campaign being waged, she recalled a statement by an officer that he could actually scent the presence of the enemy without any visible or audible signs, and that was what she was doing now. She couldn't see anything, neither could she hear a footfall on the outside staircase but she wasn't alone any longer, of that she was certain! She sniffed, perhaps, she thought, she was scenting fire and brimstone.

Oh lord! She was dramatising things again—the next thing, she'd be expecting Nicolo Gabrielli to come limping up the stairs, holding his tail well clear of the ground to save treading on it—there *were* soft footsteps on the outside staircase, they came quietly on and a dark form blocked out the light of the setting sun and cast a shadow across her spread of pastel sketches.

As a shadow had been cast across her life—she reminded herself as she felt a stirring of excitement and, grateful for the failing light, she raised a face from which all emotion, except a frown of slight displeasure, had been wiped.

'Good evening, signor.' She couldn't see his face clearly, he was standing against the glory of the sunset—only a dark shape—but she didn't have to see him to know him. Like the long ago soldier author, she *knew* when the enemy was present.

'*Buona sera*, Claudia. We meet again.' The deep, rich voice flowed over her like dark honey.

'It's inevitable, I suppose,' she shrugged. 'This is a small place, we're bound to, but as to "meeting", surely that's the wrong word.' She thought she was doing this rather well—just the right amount of chilly reproof. 'This is a private house and there's a large bell at the bottom of the staircase you've just climbed. You should have rung it—it would have saved you climbing the stairs. I'm not in the mood for visitors.' Blow hot, blow cold, that had been Maris' technique, surely she couldn't do better than emulate it.

'There's also a large, wrought iron gate rusting away in the garage.' She couldn't see his face but she could tell he was smiling, the amusement spilled over into his voice. 'It must have either fallen off or been removed some time ago and never been rehung. If it would make you feel more secure, I'll have somebody come and refit it for you.'

'Quite unnecessary,' she almost yawned in his face before she returned her attention to the sketches. She hadn't been lying when she had said she didn't want company—not his anyway— somebody like Maria perhaps, somebody un- demanding who got on with her work and didn't intrude on private thoughts. 'I don't feel in the least uneasy now. Goodnight, signor, you know the way out.' And when he didn't make a move to go, she raised a haughty eyebrow. 'Well, what are you waiting for?'

'The cock to crow, Claudia.' He moved round until the rosy light illuminated his face and she could see an almost mocking light in the dark slanting eyes. 'It crowed for St Peter—twice when he told his third lie. You shouldn't tell lies, *cara*, saying you're not nervous. Of course you are! You tried to hide it but your back was as rigid as a steel bar when you heard me on the stairs. I watched you from the end of the terrace and although I knew you'd heard me, you didn't raise your head. . . .'

'Correct, signor,' she murmured and before her brave front cracked wide open to show the quivering mass of indecision it was hiding, she motioned ruefully at the tray which held the remains of her meal. 'I was going to make some coffee, would you like some?'

'*Grazie.*' He looked speculatively at the tray and his dark brows twitched together in a slight frown. 'I leave you for a few days and this is how you eat? These scraps! Stay where you are,' as she made a movement ro rise. 'I shall make the coffee and no, I don't need any help, I know where everything is kept.'

'You would!' Despite her effort to be calm and

cool, the words came out tartly but they fell on thin air. Somehow, he was already in the kitchen, she thought he must have flowed there. One moment, he'd been standing over her and the next, he'd gone. She heard the tap running in the percolator, the clinking of crockery and the hiss of gas followed by the little pop as he lit the ring. There was a little silence broken by a soft whistling, she blinked and there was a cup and saucer at her elbow. He flowed about a bit more, silently, for all he was such a tall man and the coffee jug was on the table, another cup and saucer beside it and he was seating himself opposite her as if it was the most natural thing in the world.

'You can't take a hint, can you?' she snapped irritably and then, as a spasm of quite genuine remorse swept over her. 'I'm sorry, signor, I'm not usually so bad mannered. The fact is that I've grown used to being on my own, to pleasing myself. I've become intolerant of interference.'

'And you feel I'm interfering? That's stupid, Claudia. I told you, I feel a responsibility for you, we are acquaintances, old acquaintances and soon to be friends, I hope, so I would like you to forget your formal "signor" and call me Nico.'

'Ugh-ugh,' she wagged her head. 'Thanks but I'm afraid I don't make friends as swiftly or as easily as that. Friendship entails certain obligations—one has to like and admire a friend and at this stage, I'm not sure whether you're either likeable or admirable. I'd like to put it on ice for a while until I know you better.'

'And how will you ever know me better if you behave in this childish fashion?' he snorted. 'I came to ask you to dinner and you snap at me saying you're not in the mood for visitors—what's worse, you've already eaten, if you can call that dreary little meal eating.' He picked up the wine bottle to examine the label, 'This isn't very good, you bought it in the supermarket at Grosseto, I suppose and chose it because you liked the label.' He poured a very little into the glass she'd used and sipped at it to pull a wry face. 'The label's the best thing about it.'

'So what!' she shrugged. 'I'm your average British tourist. I can't read what's written on the label and it all tastes the same to me anyway. What's wrong with supermarkets anyway? They could have been invented solely for people like me, they make shopping so easy. I push a trolley around, collect what I want from the shelves, I don't have to strain myself asking for anything and it's all in nice hygienic wrappings and at the end, there's a girl at a till, I can read the numbers as she rings them up and hand over the right money.'

'Such a capable woman!' He was teasing and the dark brown eyes were laughing. 'Now, about this gate at the bottom of the staircase, I think perhaps I'd better have it hung for you and a new lock put on, the old one's rusted up.'

'Nonsense!' She was being contrary and she knew it—first complaining about the lack of privacy and now refusing it when it was offered. 'I'm quite capable of taking care of myself.'

'You are!' He pretended amazement. 'Let's suppose I'm an intruder. . . .'

'You are!'

'I mean one with evil intentions.' He dwelt on the word 'evil' with relish. 'I've come upstairs looking for valuables and then, I see you—a young, attractive woman, so much more attractive than the few notes in your purse. What are you going to do?'

Claudia entered into the spirit of the game. 'Kick your shins,' she replied sturdily, 'and scream my head off!'

'Kick my shins?' his eyes slid down to her soft slippers. 'In those! You'd not do a lot of damage and as for screaming, who would hear you? This little place is very isolated. Have you anything with which you could defend yourself?'

Claudia's eyes went to the tray—a couple of plates, a fork and a fruit knife—hardly an arsenal of defensive weapons. In an emergency, she would have to use the fork, the fruit knife was too blunt to do any damage—which was a pity. If it had been sharp enough, she had the idea she'd have cut Nicolo Gabrielli's throat with it for mocking her like this.

'I've been to classes on self-defence,' she offered hardily.

'And did they teach you how to jump the ten feet from the terrace to the patio below and how to land without breaking any bones?'

'That was in the third lesson,' she prevaricated. 'I had a bit of a cold and missed it. You show me how it's done!'

'Certainly not!' Nicolo was still laughing silently. 'I've never taken lessons in self-defence.'

'Oh, don't be so stupid,' she snorted softly. 'As if anybody here would break in—they're not that kind of people. . . .'

'There are others,' he pointed out gravely. 'Vagrants, perhaps a man from one of the camp sites on the coast. . . .'

'D'you know, I think you're trying to frighten me,' she scolded.

'And not before time,' he agreed. 'But you don't seem to be suitably impressed. Shall we pretend I'm the vagrant—I've had a lot to drink, I've seen this lonely little place, I've entered and found only you, young, beautiful and not Italian—everybody knows that foreign women are more free than. . . .'

'That's a lie,' she broke in indignantly.

'Perhaps,' he nodded, 'but it's a lie a man would be willing to believe, would want to believe. . . .'

As he was speaking, he'd advanced on her and Claudia had moved back from him, until now she was hard against the balustrade of the terrace so that the marble lintel on the bulging balusters was cutting cruelly into her back and she was beginning to feel afraid, although she tried to tell herself it was nonsense.

'You see,' he continued smoothly, 'I am trying to put myself in the shoes of this intruder—you will probably have money and jewellery but those can wait—there are other, sweeter things which he'll think about.'

Claudia cast an agonised glance at the table, she'd left the damn fork beside the plate—it would have been a poor weapon but she could have prodded him with the blunt tines. 'Stop this nonsense at once!' It was intended to be a command but it came out as a croaking plea and she knew how impervious he was to pleas—Maris had pleaded with him and it had got her nowhere. A glance over her shoulder—while they'd been talking, it had grown dark, a few stars had come pricking through the dark velvet of the sky and a thin sliver of moon had risen.

Below her, she could see the glimmer of the patio tiles, they looked a long way down. . . .

'Jump?' Nicolo shook his head and shrugged.

'What if you did? It might spoil a bit of the intruder's fun but then, there'd be a girl unconscious or maybe even dead on the patio and he'd have the rest of the night to rob you and a clear start to get away but perhaps he wouldn't let you jump. He'd seize you like this——' a long arm went round her waist, clipping her arms to her sides'—kiss you like this. . . .'

Claudia tried to shut her eyes but her lids wouldn't obey, they insisted on staying wide open, watching as his face came nearer. She wriggled, struggling against the power of his arm—only one arm, his other hand was beneath her chin, keeping her face tilted to his. He had a quite beautiful mouth, she thought inconsequentially—no wonder Maris had fallen for him like a ton of bricks—the top lip was wavy yet firm and the bottom lip curved fully and sensuously.

She just had time to get out, 'But this is ridic . . .' and the beautiful mouth was on hers, not hurting but with a gentle, seductive pressure. James and Maris faded from her mind, she tried to hold on to them but they sank away into a never never land. He wasn't holding her chin now, both arms were round her and she was holding her own face up. A stray moonbeam caught it, dazzling her, and she closed her eyes.

And then, the warmth and the sweetness were gone, he'd raised his head and was brushing a tear from her cheek with his finger. 'Yes, *cara*,' he was murmuring. 'Tomorrow, I'll send up a man to replace that gate and put on a new lock. You really aren't capable of looking after yourself!'

By the time she'd stumbled back to her chair, he'd gone with a soft *'Buona notte,'* and she was alone.

CHAPTER THREE

Sunlight and the endless chirruping of the
cicadas awakened Claudia, and she glanced at her
watch with a little moan. She'd overslept, which
wasn't to be surprised at—she'd been awake most
of the night. With a muzzy mind, she tried to pin
down a quotation and failed—somebody had
murdered sleep—who or what she couldn't
remember but the quotation was apt. Nicolo
Gabrielli had murdered hers in more ways than
one.

She'd lain awake in the darkness, listening—his
damn fool talk of intruders had done that—every
little sound had set her upright in bed, her hand
reaching for her big, rubber-covered torch, and
even afterwards, when she'd dragooned her mind
into sense—that nobody was going to break in to
steal or assault—there'd been the other thing to
keep her awake. The sense of shame that she could
so far forget her primary objective as to allow
herself to be manhandled, kissed and, regrettably,
enjoy it!

She groaned with weariness as she hoisted
herself out of bed and trailed to the bathroom—
her reflection in the mirror wasn't encouraging—
she looked as though she'd been awake for a
week—and she turned the cold tap of the shower
on full to step beneath an icy cascade. The cold
water had a therapeutic effect, it shocked her into
a semblance of life so that she hastily turned on
the hot tap, but there was to be no revelling in

luxury this morning. She let the jets play on her for the minimum amount of time needed to wash the soap off and hastened back to the bedroom, wrapped in a towel. She needed to think, to stand aside from herself and look at happenings objectively.

Two years and more was a long time between kisses—she pulled on a fresh pair of jeans, scowled at the stains of rose madder and cadmium yellow on the knee and reached for a clean T-shirt—and James had never been very demonstrative. A bearlike hug which nearly cracked her ribs, a kiss that went awry and landed on her nose—but the love behind those gestures had been deep and genuine and the gestures themselves had been genuine—they hadn't been the first steps in seduction as practised by a master of the craft.

Claudia didn't consider herself an authority on seducers. Nobody had ever tried to seduce her—men didn't do things like that in Chiswick—but to her way of thinking, Nicolo Gabrielli must come in the Top Twenty. He probably had a record as long as his arm otherwise he'd never have scored with her outwardly worldly wise cousin. Poor Maris, so hard, glittering and brittle on the surface yet so lacking in the everyday practicalities. Men like the Gabrielli man didn't marry their conquests, especially if the girl had been around. His marriage would be an arranged one—some pretty little convent-reared girl, stinking rich, used to doing as she was told but worldly wise in the things which mattered. She would turn a blind eye to previous affairs and she'd probably be kept so busy producing children she'd not have time to notice the succession of mistresses who shared with her her husband's favours.

By the time Claudia had brushed her hair and slapped a little cream on her face, everything was nicely arranged in her mind. Not what she would do, the way she would repay him for what he'd done to James and Maris, because she didn't know about that yet. That was a matter of opportunity, seeing a chance and taking it when it came but the immediates, they were crystal clear. Get in close, that would be her first objective, and if it cost her a few kisses, so what! Kisses didn't mean anything and if she kept her eyes shut and concentrated on James, they wouldn't even affect her.

Last night had been a mistake. He'd moved too speedily for her, caught her when she wasn't looking—when she hadn't been expecting anything more than the preliminaries of a flirtation—which was why he'd got through to her, but she wouldn't ever let it happen again.

Having dealt with her mental problems, she discovered she was as hungry as a hunter and went off to the kitchen, smiled blandly and sweetly at Maria and worked her way through hot rolls and jam, peaches sliced in yoghurt and a whole pot of coffee. Beneath her lowered lids and her innocent smile, her eyes sparkled with the light of battle and there was a soft flush in her usually pale cheeks— she was feeling better—*much* better!

Later, as she was stowing her painting gear away in the back of the Allegro, her breath erupted on the ghost of a laugh. It was hysterically funny to imagine herself as a designing woman but that was, in fact, what she was. Setting out to capture a worldly wise roué like Nicolo Gabrielli. But after all, he'd given her the idea himself so he only had himself to blame when it rebounded on his own head. And if anybody had been there to see as she drove off, they might have been surprised at the way her thin hands were clenched on the wheel and at the expression of grim determination on her face.

'You puzzle me, Claudia.' She and Nicolo were dining together at the small albergo in the village, the third or fourth time they'd done so in the last two weeks, and he was holding the bottle of wine tilted over her empty glass.

She shook her head firmly and pushed at the neck of the bottle with gentle fingers, steering it in the direction of his own glass.

'No more for me, thank you—it seems a lot more powerful than the stuff I buy. But why the puzzlement?' She let her face relax into a sweet smile and under the halo of silvery curls she looked rather angelic. 'There's nothing extra-ordinary about me, Nico.' She'd forced herself to use the name, over and over in private until it came out pat. 'I'm quite a simple person, very uncomplicated.'

'I disagree.' Dark, oblique eyes looked at her as though he was trying to get into her head to see what made her tick. 'You're many things, my dear but simple and uncomplicated—you are not!'

'Signor,' she protested and he picked her up on it straight away, his eyes glinting with a quiet mockery.

'You see! We talk about generalities and you call me Nico but when I try to talk about you, I go back to being "signor"—and after all this time.'

'A fortnight? Pooh!' she scoffed.

'More than two years,' he corrected her. 'I said we would be friends, yet still you think of me as signor, even though you manage to force a "Nico" out occasionally. And I said "friends" because, at this stage in our relationship, it sounds better. It's too early for me to say "lovers".'

Claudia smiled the madonna smile she'd been practising assiduously every day in front of her mirror, although what she said didn't match its smooth blandness. 'You're fighting dirty,' she complained softly. 'Taking advantage of the fact we're having dinner in a public place and you know I won't make a scene when there's an audience with their ears waggling to catch every word we say.'

'Mmm,' the mockery had extended from his eyes to the curve of his mouth. 'But very few people will understand and, in any case, I always fight dirty, as you call it, when I think I can't win any other way.'

'And you're not going to win any way,' she snorted softly, almost under her breath since the proprietor was advancing on them with a dishful of his speciality—grilled steak, on a bed of spinach, seasoned with pepper and lemon and garnished with parsley—something he called bistecca alla fiorentina.

'You'll like this,' Nico mocked as she inspected the contents of the dish suspiciously while he held the servers poised.

'That's what you said last time,' she snapped back and then remembered snapping was out. She was to be all sweetness and light and suffused with a glow of delicate innocence. She smiled ruefully at him. 'Tripe in a cheese and tomato sauce is very off putting.'

'It's an acquired taste,' he admitted, 'but tripe isn't unknown in England. I believe, in the north of your country it's quite popular either cooked with onions or eaten raw.'

'But I'm not from the north of my country. . . .'

'I know that,' he chuckled. 'But even in the south, I believe you have odd delicacies—jellied eels for instance?'

'Never had any, just as I've never eaten tripe,' she answered his chuckle with one of her own, following it with a little shudder. 'The look of it puts me off.'

'But tripe, done our way, is a Tuscan dish, you'll be offered it frequently and it's very popular in the trattorias.' The proprietor was still hovering and didn't go until she tried a mouthful of his bistecca and smiled at him approvingly before helping herself to crisp lettuce. Nico watched his disappearing back before continuing smoothly.

'And now, since we're once more alone,' he looked at the table with a glint in his eyes, 'shall we return to our original topic? You were saying I wouldn't win, as if we were playing some game.'

'Well, aren't we?' she raised her eyes and smiled. 'I told you, I need to like and admire my friends but when you start talking about lovers, I don't think you're admirable or likeable. I'm a very prissy lady.'

'And if I was prepared to pander to your prissiness?'

Claudia nearly choked on an unchewed piece of steak and was glad of it, it gave her time which she desperately needed. This man always moved too swiftly for her. She lacked both the experience and the know how with which to deal with him. She'd masked her real intentions and been decidedly more friendly towards him than she would have been with any other man of such short acquaintance—she didn't count what he'd done for her after the accident, it tended to make her feel guilty—but she still had the feeling she was in the grip of a current which was too strong for her, that she was already getting out of her depth. With one finger, she pushed her wine glass towards him.

'I think, after all I will have some more wine—I still can't understand why it's so much better than what I buy. . . .'

'Because, as I told you, you choose from the shelves of a supermarket and get led astray by the labels. If the bottles didn't have labels, you'd probably choose one because of the shape or the colour of the bottle. You've admitted you can't read what's printed.'

'I can't,' she admitted mournfully, 'except for "Brut". I don't know what it means but I know what it tastes like and I don't care for it. I suppose I should make an effort to learn some Italian but I don't have a flair for languages. . . .'

'And now, having successfully changed the subject, I suppose you feel safe?' His air of mockery increased. 'But you don't get off that easily, cara. Experience has taught me there's only one way to progress with a prissy lady and that's to marry her. Shall we be married, Claudia?'

Was this the way he'd operated with Maris? Was this how he'd cracked her shell, a shell toughened by the cut and thrust of the business world of fashion? But she was expected to answer and several phrases sprang to her mind. 'This is so sudden, signor,' in a die away Victorian gasp; a wise-cracking 'I'll bet you say that to all the girls'? But neither of them would do and before she could think of another, she heard her own voice, just a bit ragged, saying without any conscious volition on her part.

'I don't know but I don't think so.'

'A strange answer for a prissy lady,' he reproved her. 'You should have acted out the part—fluttered your eyelashes and blushed, said "Yes", and waited with bated breath until I made the public announcement and put a ring on your finger. That's what a simple, uncomplicated girl would have done.'

'I doubt it,' she murmured and bent over her steak once more to saw at a particularly well-done corner while she wondered if that was what Maris had done—Maris the passionate and greedy who could never bear to wait for anything she wanted.

'I said I was simple and uncomplicated,' she forced a derisory smile to her lips, 'but I didn't say I was a half-wit and,' she thought it might be worthwhile to remind him, 'I'm hardly a girl, in the strictest sense of the word. Twenty-five and a widow, signor. You were joking, of course!'

He pushed his plate aside, wiped his lips with his napkin and raised his glass to her. 'I was never more serious in all my life—now, will you call me Nico and give me a proper answer?'

'Oh dear,' she gave a little spurt of laughter. 'Was that what it was all about? Me calling you "signor"?'

'No, that wasn't what it was all about, *mia cara*,' the slanting eyes were hooded and masked by long, thick lashes which somehow made them look more Eastern than ever—reminding her that the Turks had ruled in Venice for a long time—and there was a tautness beneath the lazy grace of him so that she had the impression of a large, wild cat-like creature crouching for a spring. His heavy lids lifted and very dark brown eyes blazed into her greeny hazel ones.

'I said you puzzled me, *cara*,' she had the

impression he could see each of her thoughts as they scampered through her brain. 'Uncertain, coy and hard to please. . . .'

'I am *not* coy!' she denied it vigorously, 'and I'm certainly not hard to please. I'm the most undemanding sort of. . . .'

'Which only leaves us with the uncertainty,' he interrupted, quirking an eyebrow.

'Yours or mine?' she giggled.

'Yours, Claudia. I've never been uncertain about anything in the whole of my life. . . .'

'How fortunate for you!' she concealed the sneer in a dollop of spurious sweetness. 'To always be so certain while we lesser mortals have to shilly shally between the choices offered.'

'In a way, yes,' he accepted it as a compliment. 'I've never indulged in day dreams, my mother saw to that so you see, the word "uncertainty" isn't in my vocabulary except—except where you are concerned, my dear. I've been trying for a fortnight but I still can't understand you.'

'Then perhaps you'd better drop the acquaintance,' she suggested bravely as she helped herself to more lettuce and tomatoes. She was no longer hungry but the act of eating had its advantages. Either one concentrated on what was on the plate or fork or one made a mess of eating, and she desperately wanted to concentrate on anything or anybody except Nicolo Gabrielli, only this time, it wasn't working.

As if drawn by a magnet, her eyes lifted from the business of spearing a slice of tomato and met his and a stupid, unreasoning fear swept over her in a cold, prickling flood so that she felt as though icy hands had gripped her heart and were squeezing it until the blood drummed in her ears.

The normal, everyday sounds of the dining room—the muted chatter of other diners, the clink of glasses, the rattle of crockery and cutlery—all died away and she was alone in a dark, spinning vacuum where there was only a pair of dark, nearly black eyes watching her, gazing into her own. The darkness of the eyes increased and she realised she was watching the pupils expanding until the brown irises were no more than slim rings around a blue blackness which held a glow in their depths.

Such silly thoughts—she felt as though she was being invited in, that the glow was warmth and comfort, desire and a sweet coming together—everything she had lost when James had died—everything she had ever wanted. Then, suddenly, the dining room was back to normal. Glasses clinked against bottles, cutlery rattled against china, the hum of conversation was back and Nico was nodding at her, looking very satisfied.

'You see, Claudia, you feel it as well—this thing between us. It's like losing oneself.' There was no longer any mockery in his eyes, only a faint, wry tilt to his beautiful mouth. 'I felt it that evening, two years ago, when you came flying out of the darkness to rescue your cousin and it wasn't as though you were looking very beautiful. In fact, you looked quite plain. Your hair was wet and tumbled about by the wind and rain, your dress was rumpled and stained with that same rain and you were so nervous, your face was quite colourless and tight with strain. You looked like Medusa!'

'A rare compliment.' This time she didn't bother to disguise the sneer but she was grateful to him. For one short moment, she'd been in danger of forgetting her purpose—forgetting everything, she admitted to herself ruefully—which just showed how weak she was, how very unfitted for the task she'd set herself: to bring this man low, down on his knees where she would spit in his face before she walked away from him. But at her weakest moment, he'd reminded her of why she was here and she was back on the rails again.

'Some people wouldn't think so,' he murmured. 'But I've always thought that if Medusa wasn't the most beautiful woman on earth, beautiful enough to stop men—how do you say it?—in their tracks, then she must have had eyes which mirrored her soul—a lovely, passionate soul desperate to get out from behind the ugliness and the snakes. I've known many women, all beautiful in their different ways—I'm more than ten years older than you so it's natural that I should—and they were all attractive, but you, *cara*—with you it was different. You had something for me, something I'd wanted, been searching for for a long time. We could speak without words. . . .'

Claudia pulled herself together and became prosaic, it was the only way she felt she could deal with a situation which was rapidly getting out of hand.

'I remember being very hungry,' she said flatly. 'We, James, my husband, and I hadn't time for anything but the small meal on the plane; we'd only been married that morning,' speaking about it brought it all back; all the bitterness and pain and she revelled in it. 'When Maris made that detour to your place, we thought she was taking us to one of her parties. I always get pale when I'm starving. There, has that cleared up any of your uncertainties? And now,' she grabbed at the menu and hid behind it, 'which cheese do you recommend?'

'Coward!' He hooked a finger over the top of the menu and prised it from the position where she was holding it like a shield, but she was careful. This time, her eyes rose no higher than the collar of his white shirt. He wasn't wearing a tie, only a silky looking cravat tucked into the open neck so that she could see the brown column of his throat. A little pulse was beating beneath the skin and she stared at it, fascinated. The skin was as smooth as a woman's, there was a faint film of perspiration on it and the pulse was beating—beating——

'Mozarella, or, if you wish to be truly adventurous, you can try some caciocavallo, which is made with mares' milk. But wouldn't you like to try a dessert? They make a superb panforte di Siena here, it's a cake with candied fruit, cloves and pimento and the sweetness makes it good for eating a strong cheese afterwards. Nothing venture, nothing gain.' She flushed at the amusement in his voice. He wasn't talking about cheese and they both knew it.

Later, outside the back of the Villa Cristal, he switched off the engine of the black car and then sat with his hands on the wheel. 'Are you going to invite me in for a cup of coffee?' His voice came velvet upon the dark velvet of the night, even the cicadas had ceased their interminable chirruping and everything seemed to be still with a stillness which was waiting.

In the darkness, Claudia could just make out the white walls and the dark sprawl of a rampant, flowering creeper where it covered the side of the small house. The moon, well past full, hadn't risen yet and the wildness of the garden couldn't be

seen, but there was a delicious scent from a great
bush of rosemary mixed in with the spicier,
sweeter, more pungent smell from a bed of dark
red geraniums. Within those white walls lay safety
and Claudia longed for it—she hadn't been feeling
very safe for the past hour or so.

'No,' she hadn't said a word so he answered his
own question. 'I'll forego the coffee, you don't
seem to have the way of making it properly. You
always give me a thin and bitter brew.'

'Always is three times in two weeks,' she felt it
necessary to point out. She thought she was doing
fine. 'That's hardly a record.'

'You'll learn,' she heard his soft laugh. 'Emilia
shall teach you, but while you are learning one
thing from her, there is something I can teach. . . .'

Claudia knew what was going to happen—in a
way, it was what she'd hoped would happen.
Getting in close hadn't been a problem after all, it
was as though all the fates had been on her side—
or were they? Because, now it was happening, she
no longer wanted it, perversely and reluctantly she
had to admit it. She couldn't cope with it. She'd
also had a semi-proposal of marriage and she
couldn't cope with that, either. What should have
been her high spot, the time when she should have
been flushed with victory, had turned out to be a
low and her triumph had tasted bitter as gall. She
just wasn't the type to make love promiscuously.

With an incoherent murmur, she strove to push
him away as he leaned over to put his arm about
her but she might just as well have pushed against
the tide to stop it coming in. He wasn't brutal,
didn't hurt her but he was there, firm and
demanding and he didn't rush things, get them
over quickly.

'Why are you trembling?' His breath was warm against her neck. 'No, *cara*, this isn't the preliminary to a seduction scene. I'll wed you first and bed you afterwards—that's how they would say it in English, isn't it?'

Claudia burrowed her face deeper into the cloth of his jacket where she thought it would be safe and muttered into the thick white linen.

'Too old-fashioned. Try "stay cool" or I may be out of date with that one. Times change and so does the vernacular.'

'Mmm,' he thought about it and discarded it. 'I don't like that, I prefer my version. I'm rather old-fashioned myself. I read it once in a book and it appealed to me.'

'And of course, you've stuck to it!' She was lured out of her hiding place by the chance to cross swords with him.

'Not always.' He didn't sound regretful, rather he was laughing, although whether at her or himself, it was difficult to tell. 'I'm not exactly proud of some of the things I've done but I don't think I'm ashamed of any of them. Shall we now continue on more delectable lines, we can get so much further with actions than with words.'

'I prefer the words. . . .'

'But I'm at a disadvantage.' Again he was amused. 'You won't or can't speak mine so I have to speak yours and although I'm good at it, there are some phrases one doesn't learn in conversations with business men.'

'Oh, I'm sure you can manage beautifully.' She tried to push herself away from but but the arm about her tightened. 'Just use the words you'd use if you were trying to seduce one of those businessmen's secretaries, one who didn't speak

Italian. You're handicapped, I admit—there's no soft light or sweet music so your soulful looks won't have the same effect but that's only a minor obstacle. Do you love me?' It would be good to have him admit it.

'I don't know.' He was aggravatingly calm. 'We have something, Claudia, and whatever it is, it's strong enough to have lasted two years. I think we could be profoundly happy together.'

'Or profoundly miserable,' she argued, 'and really, I think I'm too tired to go into the pros and cons of it now. I'm glad you haven't tried to swear undying love, that's what most of you Latin lovers do, isn't it? Because I wouldn't have believed you—remember, I told you, I'm twenty-five years old and a widow; not a starry eyed girl looking for romance.'

'You are the most ridiculous woman.' His arm tightened further and although she kept her body rigid, she was drawn firmly against him. There were long, strong fingers under her chin and what little light there was was blotted out by his head. 'I told you words would be useless, *gioia*; we can solve it much more quickly my way, this way. . . .'

Claudia tried to pretend it was James kissing her—so stupid—James had never kissed her like this—his cool mouth moving over hers until it felt as though every bone in her body had melted, that she was a slack, mindless thing without the power to move. Her mind had closed down, she couldn't even think, only feel. Feel an urgency uncoiling itself deep in her stomach to spread tentacles of heat through every nerve in her body, taking her over so that she couldn't think of anything except to get closer to him, to let the heat go on warming her, bringing back life to a dead thing and suddenly, she was afraid. Right in the middle of bliss, the fear struck, making her wrench away from his marauding mouth and hands and cower away from him with wide, frightened eyes and a shaking hand over her quivering lips.

'Cara?' His voice came in the darkness, a little puzzled and then filled with certainty and something like triumphant laughter. 'Oh *cara*, twenty-five years old, a widow and still a virgin—this is the girl who's not a girl any longer? But of course, I should have known, you're not the type to indulge in pre-marital sex—for you, it would all have to be right and afterwards, there wasn't time. . . .'

'That's a bloody indelicate thing to say.' She found her voice and with it, some courage although inside, she was still a quivering, aching, terrified mess.

'I'm a—er—bloody indelicate man. . . .'

'And what right, what reason have you to suppose that?' She could feel tension building up in her and her voice was almost shrill.

'I don't *suppose* anything,' he returned imperturbably. 'I *know*. Claudia, my dear, there's no reason for you to be afraid. I won't. . . .'

'You're damn well right, you won't!' she snapped. 'Now, let me out of this car, damn you.' She jiggled frantically at the door handle and almost screamed when it refused to move. 'This is the finish,' she raged. 'You can transfer your responsibility to somebody else—somebody who really needs it. I never want to see you again—not ever!'

Under her hand, the handle went down and the door swung open to set her free and she was running, stumbling in the darkness. Bushes and branches clawed at her, she tripped and fell, there was the pungent fragrance of geraniums to tell her she'd made a mess of the sweet-smelling border, but she struggled to her feet.

Safety was only a few yards away and she headed for it like a frightened animal. Her toe caught against the bottom step up to the patio and careless of dignity, she went up the rest on all fours to wrench open the door of her bedroom and slam it behind her, her fingers frantically scrabbling as the key reluctantly turned. Oil that tomorrow!

An hour later, she was still lying fully clothed on her bed, eyes wide and staring into the blackness while she tried to sort herself out. She'd spoiled everything by over-reacting and now that the reaction had set in, she could see clearly where she'd gone wrong. She'd let emotion take the place of disciplined reason—she'd had revenge there, in the palm of her hand and she'd blown it! She could have been well on the way to making him suffer and she'd ruined everything. It would be impossible to go back, to regain the previous, almost friendly relationship, so she might as well pack up and go home.

Even this thought didn't stir her to do more than scramble from the bed, remove her clothes, take a hasty shower and crawl back into bed to almost laugh aloud at her magnificent pretensions. She, Claudia, was to have been a kind of St Michael with a flaming sword of vengeance to turn the Gabrielli man out of his earthly paradise— because he'd no right to be happy or content when she had lost everything.

And what had happened? He'd demonstrated that she was mistaken, she hadn't lost everything, that there was a lot in life she knew nothing about.

Her mind might tell her everything was over for her, that life had little to offer, but her stupid body was saying something different. Worse than that, she was beginning to realise revenge was an unsatisfactory thing. It wouldn't heal her hurts and it wouldn't compensate for her loss. The past was dead, James and Maris were dead—nothing she could do would alter that or make her feel any better about it.

Go home! The idea took root and started to grow. Go home, make a new life for herself, pick up the threads or—or she might end up like Maris, a pitiful, pleading thing. . . .

CHAPTER FOUR

MORNING came at last and with a new sense of purpose, Claudia set about what she had to do. It was Maria's day off and the little villa had to be left spotless and shining. When she'd finished the housework, she'd pack, load the Allegro and drive straight down to Rome. Once there, she'd put up at a modest hotel and tomorrow, she'd phone Maris' lawyer—she had his name and the phone number of his office. They could make arrangements to sell the apartment—she could stay in it for a couple of days, clear out Maris' personal things—something she ought to have done ages ago and then, back to London. All ties with the past cut quickly and cleanly—something else she should have done ages ago.

Since it was Maria who brought the bread and milk each day, Claudia breakfasted scrappily on stale bread with jam and black coffee before getting down to work, coming to the conclusion after less than an hour of mopping acres of marble floors that Maria earned every penny she was paid. It looked and sounded a lot but it worked out at considerably less than the charring rate at home, with few modern conveniences.

After an equally scrappy lunch, she stripped her bed and tidied the bedroom, folding the soiled linen into a pile and pinning an envelope containing a hefty tip to the top sheet before she started toing and froing between the wardrobe and chest of drawers and her cases which were open on the bed. One suitcase was already packed and she'd nearly finished the second. The little villa was immaculate, swept and garnished and in another hour she would be on her way—the bonnet of the Allegro firmly pointed in the direction of Rome with her foot hard down on the accelerator.

She trailed back to the wardrobe, reaching inside it for the remaining linen suit, grabbed at it and stooped to pick up an overlooked pair of shoes.

'You're going somewhere?' Nico's voice came from behind her and she spun round from her stooped position, squeaking with pain as her elbow caught the wardrobe door.

'Oooooh!—Yes—er—a letter this morning . . . and I thought I told you never to come here again!'

'You should try to lie more convincingly.' There was no gentle mockery in his eyes, only a hard light which she identified, or thought she identified, as temper. 'For a lie to be good,' he continued with a rasp in his voice, 'it has to be well thought out—there must be a bit of truth in it. . . .'

'Oh, I haven't your experience,' she kept it airy. 'What's wrong with my having a letter this morning? I often get one from London. I'm not entirely without friends, you know.' And she tilted her nose as high as it would go.

'Certainly,' he agreed softly, in complete contrast to the gathering shrillness in her voice. 'But all your letters go to the estate office in the village. Maria brings them up to you when she comes. Today is her day off so I looked for them myself when I was there and there was nothing for you. If there had been, I would have brought it myself.' He relieved her of the suit and shoes and tossed them carelessly on to the pile in the case. 'Shall we have the truth for a change?'

Claudia nursed her elbow and scowled at him. 'You're calling me a liar, signor?'

'Yes and not a very good one. I told you that you puzzled me and now I'd like some answers to a few questions, for instance—why you came here at all. Oh yes,' as her mouth opened to give him a stinging reply telling him to mind his own business, 'we know all about your painting, the way you earn your living—the fact that this little house belongs to you, but that doesn't explain why you're here, does it? In a place which must hold painful memories for you.'

'I'm so glad you remembered that,' she cooed as softly as a dove and she marched across to the case and started folding things only to have a firm hand on her shoulder whirl her round.

'Stop it!' he almost snarled. 'You're an adept at changing the conversation but this time, I won't allow it. You're going to marry me and I insist. . . .'

'You can insist till you're black in the face,' she shouted him down, 'and I'm *not* going to marry you—I wouldn't, not if you were hung all over with diamonds!'

'Thank you, signora,' he took it very well. 'Although there is a more gracious way of refusing my offer—I can only suppose you've been badly brought up!' And he stalked to the door, shutting it behind him just in time. The shoes she hurled after him bounced on the panels of mosquito netting and fell harmlessly to the floor.

While she was retrieving the shoes, putting them and the linen suit tidily in the case and all the time she was struggling to fasten it, she heard the starting motor of his car whining and then faltering and at last, overcome by curiosity, she went up on to the terrace and peered over the balustrade to where the two cars were parked side by side. She watched him get out from behind the wheel to raise the bonnet to delve inside and crowed triumphantly.

'Flashy and unreliable!' she called out to him and then went back to collect her cases which she carried out and stuffed into the back of the Allegro. But there wasn't so much triumph in it after all, although she felt herself bound to make the most of what there was.

'Can I give you a lift somewhere?' she enquired sweetly.

He straightened up with a small piece of engine in his hand, complicated and a bit oily, there were smudges on his fingers. 'You can, signora.' He held it out for her to see, a round thing with a wire dangling. 'I need another one of these, I have it in my garage and if you'd be so kind. . . .'

'With pleasure, signor,' the 'badly brought up' bit was still rankling and her smile was nearly a snarl. 'I'll overlook your rudeness and be generous. I'll take you up to your villa, wait for you and bring you back as far as the road. You'll have to walk the last couple of kilometres along the lane I'm afraid, but I really can't spare the time. I want to be in Rome before it gets dark.'

'*Grazie*, signora.' He was formal to the point of woodenness. 'You are too kind.' He folded himself up in the front passenger seat and when the Allegro started at the first turn of the key, her triumph was complete and she backed around the bulk of his car with a scream of gears.

The Villa Gabrielli held no fears for her now—she could almost believe it was a dream that she'd stood with Maris at the top of the shallow flight of steps—the stout door, the old-fashioned bellpull, these had haunted her sleeping hours for two years but they never would again. If nothing else good had come of this hare-brained scheme she'd thought up, that had. In future she'd sleep calmly and well with no ghosts to keep her awake or even wake her to screaming fright and she pulled up in front of the door with another screeching flourish, only this time, it was the brakes.

'Shall you be long?' she demanded peremptorily.

'A little while only.' He was almost soothing. 'You'll become very hot if you stay out here in this car and although I know it might give you pain, stir old memories, I'd like you to accept my hospitality while you wait—a cool drink perhaps? You see, I might have to make another connection but it shouldn't take me long.'

Claudia nodded serenely. She was going to prove to him and to herself that nothing, but nothing in his house held any terror for her and after scrambling out of the Allegro, she walked after him composedly, allowed herself to be shown into a cool salotto and with a meaningless smile, she sank gratefully on to one of the couches. Her head was beginning to ache and she'd never felt so weary in all her life, so that when Emilia pattered in with a tray containing a jug of lemon juice and a tall glass filled with crushed ice, she smiled gratefully, managed a soft *grazie*, which she meant from the bottom of her heart and even managed a smile before she rooted in her bag for a couple of aspirin.

The granita slid smoothly and coldly down her dry throat and when she'd drained it, there was still enough ice left in the glass for a refill. 'Relax,' she told herself. 'You've a long way to drive and you didn't sleep much last night,' and she put the glass back on the tray and let herself go limp against the fat cushions. The room was gloriously cool and dim after the blinding light and suffocating heat outside, she could feel the tension draining out of her and wonder of wonders, the dull, dead heaviness which had filled her for so long was gone. She felt light and free and she didn't want to hurt anybody any more.

The light shining in her eyes woke her, a soft, restful light and she raised her head as Nicolo gently shook her shoulder.

'*Cara*,' he murmured softly. 'Wake up. It's past seven o'clock and you'll wish to bathe and change before dinner.'

What had started out as a languid movement of her head became a spasmodic jerk as the words sank in and she sat upright so quickly, it made her head swim.

'Gone seven!' her voice cracked. 'But I'm driving to Rome, I'm leaving. Damn you, you knew that so why did you let me sleep? Now, I'll have no time to get a meal on the road and all the hotels will be full and you *know* I can't speak Italian. . . .'

Another face swam into focus over his shoulder and she peered at it belligerently. There was more than a resemblance. The two faces, his and the female one behind him could have been cast from the same mould. The lady's hair was the same guinea gold although a bit faded by time and the eyes were exactly alike, almond shaped and set

aslant under straight dark brows. She watched
Nicolo turn to it and although she heard what he
said, she couldn't believe her ears.

'You see, Mama? I can't thank you enough for
being here. We'll speak English, I think whenever
possible, Claudia understands very little Italian
and I think she's sufficiently confused already—
driving in this heat and after working like a
housemaid all morning—she said there was so
much she had to do before she could leave the
little house.'

A long, slender hand with smooth fingers and
delicately tinted nails reached for her wrist, felt at
her pulse and a cool, amused voice gave the
verdict. 'Tumultuous, *caro*. Your Claudia is
certainly in no condition to drive. You should
have fetched her and not allowed her. . . .'

Claudia was inclined to agree with the lady—she
could feel and hear the blood thundering in her
ears—a heavy, rather fast boom—boom—boom.
She took a deep breath to steady herself and
became chilly and concise.

'There was nothing wrong with me when I drove
here,' she said it to both of them and then singled
out Nicolo with a smouldering look which spelled
trouble. 'Your car broke down if you remember
and I gave you a lift. . . .'

She watched as Nicolo's eyebrows rose. 'My
car broke down? *Piccola*, you've been dreaming.
My car has never broken down.' The mockery
was back, curving his lips and setting a sparkle
in his eyes. 'It may be flashy but it's very
reliable, which is why I chose it in preference to
many others. Why! More than two hours ago, I
sent it down to the village to bring Doctor
Calzino here for dinner. As one of Mama's

oldest friends, I wished him to be here tonight to share our joy.'

The soft, feminine fingers at her wrist had been replaced by younger, masculine and more powerful ones and she was feeling the power now and the mockery, he was ablaze with it.

'A mild sedative, d'you think, Mama? Nothing too severe or Claudia won't be able to eat her dinner—perhaps if you consulted with the *dottore*. . . .' and as the tall, still slender woman nodded and went out of the room, Nicolo turned back to her and she winced away from the rage in his eyes.

'Claudia.' All the gentle tenderness had gone from his voice, it was cold and sharp—almost as it had been that night when he'd spoken so brutally to Maris. 'I took the liberty yesterday afternoon of phoning my mother in Venice to tell her I intended asking you to marry me. . . .'

'Then you jumped the gun.' She struggled upright away from the comfort of the fat pillows and put up her hands, one on either side of her head to stop the pain pounding at her temples. 'You'll just have to tell her the truth,' she muttered.

'I can't do that,' he shook his head. 'Mama looks well enough but she has a heart condition and already, she's overtaxed herself. Leaving Venice last night, travelling all night and most of today—she arrived about two hours ago, which is the real reason I sent for the *dottore*, not for you. You may be a bit agitated but you're as strong as a horse. But I thought, as we're going to be married, we might as well make it public so there will be a few others here for dinner besides the *dottore*. The priest—he'll have to know—a few friends to make up the numbers, Mama will be expecting a glittering occasion. . . .'

'I won't have it,' she broke in on him fiercely. 'It's all a fiction and I shall tell them so. I shall also tell them you got me here by a trick, a dirty, low down, lousy trick. You kidnapped me! And if you won't tell them, I shall!'

'I kidnapped you, brought you here by trickery?' Nicolo didn't look innocent, he couldn't, but he did manage an excellent expression of bafflement. 'Claudia, *cara*, you've been too long in the sun. You came here of your own free will, nobody forced you to come. You entered my house on your own two feet, nobody carried you in, bound and gagged. . . .'

'You said your car wouldn't start,' she interrupted. 'You waved a thing with a bit of wire at me. . . .'

'You came here as my guest,' he corrected, 'and you're staying until we can agree on our future together. . . .'

'But why?' Her burst of temper had subsided and bewilderment had taken its place, maybe she was seeking reassurance, she didn't know—she didn't know anything any more except that she knew she didn't know! 'You don't really want to marry me,' she muttered it, possibly in the hope that he'd contradict her—if so, she was disappointed.

'No, I don't think I do,' he shrugged. 'There are several things about you which don't appeal to me but Mama seems to approve of you which is by the way of being a minor miracle. She's never approved of any of my lady friends before.'

'And I should be flattered?' Claudia ran a nervous hand through her silver curls so that they stood out like a halo about her head. 'Look,' she tried to sound reasonable. 'Why don't you let me go? You've just said you don't think you want to marry me and I assure you, I don't want to marry you—I don't want to marry anybody, I'm quite happy as I am. All right,' as she saw his brows draw into a scowl, 'I'll put on a show for your mother, if that's what you want although I'm going to look like Cinderella—I didn't bring "occasion" clothes with me but I'll look as festive as I can for this evening and tomorrow, when all the hooh hah's died down, I'll get on my way to Rome and when I've finished my bit of business there, I'll go back to England. After that, it'll be easy. We'll discover we made a mistake—that we aren't suited. We'll have second and third thoughts—you've already had a few—you said there are several things about me that don't appeal. . . .'

'And you're offended because I don't think you perfect. I knew, as I said it, that you'd be angry. . . .'

'Well!' she brought it out on a gasp of anger. 'Let me tell you, there's very little about you that appeals to me! For one thing, you've far too high an opinion of yourself. . . .'

'And you've been less than honest with me, I think,' and at the expression in his eyes, she flushed. But how could she have told him—she tried the words out in her mind.

'My original intention was to make you suffer as I've suffered,' and then she'd go on—'It's your fault that James, my husband and Maris are dead—you were brutal to her—I don't know what you said but I heard the way you said it—you upset her very much, so much that she wasn't really fit to drive—that's how the accident happened. You couldn't be more to blame if you'd pushed them over that cliff yourself! *You* killed James and Maris, *you* made me a widow!'

But things like that couldn't be said, they sounded too hysterical, too over dramatised and in any case, her lust for revenge had died the death. It had been an hysterical thing which had kept her going through two years—she realised now she must have been slightly mad with grief and loneliness. Time heals—damn her gran for always having a saying to fit the circumstances and damn herself for always remembering. . . .

Nicolo was speaking and she'd missed the first part but she caught the last words just as his mother came in with a small phial of tablets

'. . . so, one day, you'll tell me and then, we might get somewhere. Ah, Mama, you've found something?'

'A mild tranquiliser only. Old Calzino says it can't possibly do any harm.' His mother nodded her stately head. 'Nico, go and attend to our guests while Claudia and I have a little talk. Go now! How do you expect women to talk together when you stand listening to every word!'

There was a cheerful smile on Signora Gabrielli's face as the door closed behind him and she turned back to Claudia.

'You don't want a pill, do you? I hope not because I've no intention of giving you one. My little act with the bottle was only what you call "window dressing" for Nico's benefit. You look far too sensible to dose yourself indiscriminately. Emilia is going to bring us some tea, which I think will be much better for you. . . .'

Apparently, Nico's Mama was a voluble lady

and Claudia laid her head back against the cushions and let the tide of talk wash over her in a soothing flood.

'I was beginning to despair of Nico.' His mother sipped her tea and sighed with satisfaction. 'You're feeling better now? Yes, I thought you would. So many women, you understand but all unsuitable, he knew that of course but he has great charisma so it was only natural—to be expected—I stopped worrying about him years ago. I never met most of them so I knew you were different when he told me about you. You've finished your tea? Good, then we shall go to your room and you will take a bath—one always feels better after a bath. No, don't hurry, there's plenty of time. When I was young, I rushed—one misses so much but now, I go slowly, savouring every moment—it's a pity we can't be born with wisdom.'

'And you're a painter,' Signora Gabrielli hopped from one subject to another with the agility of a grasshopper. 'What do you think of these?' her hand swept round, indicating portraits in gilded frames. 'Terrible, aren't they, not a good one among them—stiff, wooden men and plump, simpering ladies—that's about the best, the lady in green. I suppose the artist did what he could but nothing could ever have made that woman look other than a self-satisfied sheep.'

Claudia was glad she wasn't expected to admire. As Nicolo's mother said, there was very little admirable in any of the portraits—the sitters all looked like sheep but whoever had painted the woman in green had been a good technician. The satin of the gown looked real, bright where the light caught it and deepening almost to black in the folds and the lace had been painted meticulously as had the heavy, emerald and gold jewellery but it was as the signora said—under the complicated hair-do of glossy black ringlets and braids was a boney, pale, smug little face without character and—she thought—very little brain behind it.

There were more portraits lining the walls as the signora took Claudia upstairs and she waved a negligent hand towards them. 'I can never understand this desire to perpetuate the commonplace. My family were all good looking but then, I am a Venetian—a different breed and I pride myself that I've passed on our looks to Nicolo—our looks and our business acumen. You should see Sandro, Nicolo's nephew—a pretty boy now but the signs are there—he's going to be fat like his mother, fat and undistinguished—another sheep to join the fold. I'm not tiring you, I hope. I know I talk too much. . . .'

Claudia shook her head with a smile. 'Not a bit but I was thinking you'd be a good head for August. My calendar,' she explained, 'pastel heads, one for each month. . . .' She was gabbling and she knew it but what else could she do? If there had been a silent moment, a pause, she would have opened her mouth and the truth would have come tumbling out and this charming woman's dreams would all be spoiled—better to gabble aimlessly than that.

The signora took the whole thing very seriously. 'September, I think and you shall pay me a small fee. I shall also expect a free copy of the calendar when it's printed. I shall make you a very good September.'

While they'd been talking, the signora had been leading the way down passages, through doors, along terraces. 'A rabbit warren, I always said so. Thank god, I never had to live in it, ah, here we are.' She opened a door and led Claudia into an enormous bedroom, looking around it critically. 'Too much furniture,' she gave her verdict, 'but you will be comfortable, I think. The bathroom is through there,' she waved at a door, 'and your cases have been brought up. Shall we see what you have to wear?'

Nobody could have accused Claudia of being overdressed for dinner, but she consoled herself she didn't look too bad. A simple cream linen shift—a cast-off from Maris and nobody could ever fault the clothes she designed—her only decorations, a string of old amber beads with some earrings of amber drops within a cluster of gold leaves and she thanked her lucky stars she'd been firm about the hat. Her face was smooth under the light dusting of powder, it didn't look in the least like a patchwork quilt as she'd feared.

A knock at the door disturbed her concentration just as she was putting on some lipgloss and nervousness sent a streak of pale shininess across her cheek as her hand slipped. She was so nervous and uncertain that even this small upset brought tears welling into her eyes and she reached for a tissue to wipe it off before she called 'come in' but calling wasn't necessary. Nicolo was already in and laughing at her chagrin. He had his back to the door and was looking quite startlingly handsome in formal evening clothes. At the sight of him, her nervousness changed to irritability.

'Did you have to doll yourself up like that tonight of all nights?' In the mirror, her eyes glowered at him. 'I told you I was short of that kind of clothes! I shall have a tray in my room, if it's not too much trouble.'

'Far too much trouble.' He came towards her until he was just behind her and their two faces were reflected together in the glass. 'Mama tells me she personally selected that dress. Simple and elegant, she said and eminently suitable for a young lady taking her second shot at matrimony.'

'It's a hand-me-down from Maris,' Claudia was belligerently frank. 'One of her discards in fact.' She gave him a tartly sweet smile. 'Second hand, like its wearer. I shan't do you much credit.'

'But is the wearer second hand, that is the question?' The mockery was back and going full blast so that she felt like turning and scratching his eyes out. 'I'm practically sure she isn't. When a woman has deep feelings and doesn't know what to do with them, I take that as a good sign.'

Claudia picked up the hairbrush, had second thoughts about what she'd do with it and commenced, vigorously to ruin her hairdo— brushing out the feathery curls which she'd coaxed on to her forehead and, with them, the film of hairspray which would have kept them in place, neatly covering a hairline scar which the surgeons had said would vanish with time.

'Damn you.' She flushed and the scar stood out, white against pink. She'd never thought she blushed right up to her hairline. 'What do you want anyway from a woman who has qualities which don't appeal to you?'

'That still rankles?' He took her hand and held it firmly before she could do any more damage with the hairbrush. 'You made me angry, *cara*, I meant to put it more politely. Shall we forget it was said, we were neither of us on our best behaviour. I came to bring you this,' he produced a ring. 'Mama hoped you wouldn't mind wearing one of hers until I give you your own.' Camlly, he held on to her hand firmly despite her struggles and pulled off the wide gold band of her wedding ring. It came off easily, her fingers, like the rest of her, had grown thin—and she felt the borrowed ring slide on in its place.

'I shall replace it of course,' he continued as with an unexpected delicacy, he replaced her wedding ring on the third finger of her right hand. 'I thought emeralds, do you like them or would you prefer something else?'

Claudia looked down at the ring on her finger, the setting was so long it completely covered the bottom joint and it was studded with seed pearls and small turquoise—not valuable except that it might be an antique, it had that look of loving workmanship which was missing in a modern ring—it was the only thing which stopped her tearing it off and stamping on it.

'I'm not interested in jewellery,' she muttered, 'and,' her voice strengthened, 'as I've no intention of accepting any from you, I don't see much point in this.'

'But I have to know,' he was reasonable. 'A ring you will wear for the rest of your life—you have to like it and emeralds would suit you. A necklace of them would make your eyes look very green.'

'Why are you doing this to me?' She heard herself half sobbing the words and was ashamed of herself—she'd always despised women who wept, used tears as a weapon.

'I'm trying to make you see the truth.' He slid his arms around her unresisting body and his hands were very gentle. 'We've something,

Claudia. It was there that first night we met, it's still there.'

'I felt nothing,' she denied it forcefully but she wouldn't look at him as she said it because she was lying. She *had* felt something but it hadn't been anything tender or worthwhile. She'd felt a twisted hate cramping in her stomach and that had been before James and Maris had been killed. She'd hated this man for reducing her arrogant, volatile cousin to a pleading *thing* and she'd built on that original hate until it occupied her life and every thought, waking or sleeping.

But it hadn't lasted—she was sorry in a way about that. It would be so much easier if she'd gone on hating, wanting to hurt. Hating somebody you didn't know was the easiest thing in the world but once you knew a person, it became difficult— hate warped and shrivelled things till they were twisted out of recognition—it had warped her but she was free of it now.

There were always two sides to anything and Maris had never been an angel of light and—her brow furrowed as she remembered things—had she forgotten them deliberately to add fuel to her rage of despair? Maris so cowed, so beaten—it had come as a shock to see her normally hard-hearted cousin brought so low, reduced to hysterical weeping, James huddled silent in the rear seat, swamped with embarrassment—he'd always hated scenes—he'd said he loved her because she never made any! And Maris recovering some of her bounce—rebounding from hopeless misery to a kind of vicious 'I'll-pay-him-back-if-it's-the-last-thing-I-do' attitude. Very much as she, Claudia, had been for the last couple of years. But it was to the Gabrielli man she owed her life and that was a debt she could partly pay although she didn't suppose he'd be in the least grateful.

'All right,' she lifted her head but avoided the dark, oblique eyes which seemed to see too much for her peace of mind. 'You can get whichever ring you like although I shan't ever wear it so you'd be better off saving your money—but I won't let you down tonight, I promise. And I won't upset your mother—I couldn't do that anyway, I like her too much. The only thing I can't understand is how she ever managed to produce a son like you.'

'Always a sting in the tail,' he murmured, 'but you'll wear my mother's ring—that way it will look more convincing in case you can't manage the proper dazed look of happiness.'

'Happiness,' she scoffed softly, 'after what I've been through?'

'Yes,' he tucked her hand beneath his arm and commenced to lead her from the room. 'You forget, I know what you've been through but that was all two years ago and you're young. The young soon forget.'

'Do they indeed!' If it hadn't been for the fact she was wearing strappy white sandals with tall, fragile heels, she'd have stamped on his feet for being so insensitive.

'They do if they are normal.' He was marching her off at a tremendous rate and she was hard put to keep up with him.

'You're suggesting I'm not?' It came out as a gasp, partly because she was out of breath but more because she didn't like the inference.

'Of course you're normal.' He stopped as they entered another passage and pulled her round to face him. 'You have all the normal responses except you seem to take offence very easily. What is being done is for your good, Claudia, you need—er—straightening out. . . .'

'And you've elected yourself to do the straightening?' Her voice rose to a squeak of indignation.

'Certainly! I'm the only one who can,' he riposted. 'You've become a selfish little introvert—to be expected after all you've gone through. You have to learn to live again, live with people, so put a smile on your face, stop looking at me as though I was diseased and we'll start on your first lesson!'

CHAPTER FIVE

'THAT was good, wasn't it?' Signora Gabrielli sighed with satisfaction as she waved the last dinner guest goodbye, to take Claudia's arm and led her back from the steps outside the door where mosquitos were whining voraciously, into the comparative safety of the salotto. 'And you, Claudia—you were just right. Calm, composed, neither embarrassed nor shy—so many girls giggle or look coy.'

'Your ring, signora,' Claudia slid it from her finger and proffered it. 'Thank you for the loan.'

'A trifle.' Nicolo's Mama waved it aside. 'Not valuable—perhaps a little as an antique, you understand—but decorative and pretty to look at. Keep it, a small gift from me to my son's *fidanzata*. A pity you could not have had a family ring, there was a lot of jewellery, most of it very ugly but Sandro has it all. I suppose he'll deck that milk-and-water ninny he's marrying with it,' she snorted. 'Another bleating little sheep!'

'Mama!' Nicolo managed to make it sound almost amused but there was a warning note at the back of it. 'Claudia isn't interested in our family affairs. She's not burdening me with a clutch of relatives so the least I can do is refrain from boring her with mine. Except you, of course.'

'But as one of the family she'll have to know,' his mother sniffed.

'And she will but not yet,' he was quite firm. 'I shall tell her whatever is necessary, but not until it's necessary.'

78

'Yes,' his mother nodded sagely. 'Perhaps that would be the wisest thing. Claudia might have an aversion to decadent halfwits.' She gave Claudia a proud smile. 'My son takes after me,' and her smile became almost smug, 'both in looks and brains.'

Claudia, full of good food and fortified by two glasses of wine and a small brandy which she'd dunked in her coffee, lowered her voice to a sexy drawl. 'A paragon, signora. Handsome *and* intelligent,' she slanted a glance up at her *fidanzato* who was looking thunderous. 'Aren't I the lucky one! What more could a girl ask for?'

'Your bedtime, Mama,' Nicolo offered an arm and his mother took it reluctantly.

'I'm not at all tired,' she protested but then, with a swift glance up at her son's forbidding face, 'very well, if you say so, Nico,' and before Claudia's eyes, she changed from a vibrant, amusing person into a weary and rather pathetic, well past middle-aged lady. Claudia watched the transformation, at first with shock and then, seeing the wicked droop of an eyelid, with amusement. Signora Gabrielli didn't miss a trick—there wouldn't be any scoldings from her masterful son—this was a lady who could and did—when she wished—get away with murder!

When they had gone, Claudia lay back in a deep chair, her head against the fat, cushioned back and watched the light bulbs sending green, blue, purple and red spears of light through the crystal drops of the chandelier as they moved gently in a current of air. Everything was so peaceful—it was hard to realise she was in the middle of a battle—almost impossible to accept she was here against her will. The silence of the house stole over her, lapping her in content and then everything splintered into sharp edges as Nicolo came back into the room and Claudia thought she heard a trumpet in her mind calling her to battle.

'I'm too tired to fight tonight,' she complained involuntarily.

'Who said anything about fighting?' He stood over her, looking down at her quizzically.

'Nobody,' she grumbled, 'but it's there, isn't it? You've made me stay here when I wanted to go to Rome—cause enough, I should say for a bit of warfare. I've been pleasing myself what I do for quite a while and I don't take kindly to bullying.'

'Your husband didn't bully you?'

'Certainly not!' James swam up into her consciousness, his outline was dim but she could hear his voice—'Anything you say, darling'; 'You arrange it, my love'; and almost the last thing he'd said—'Good lord, your cousin's a bit of a tartar, I hope it's not a family failing!' That had been when, with the clamour of the storm all about them, Maris had stormed out of the car and up the steps to the door of this house, hurrying through the wild, wet darkness because, although it wasn't sensible, it was what she had made up her mind to do and nothing would stop her.

Maybe she, Claudia, was more like Maris than she'd thought, it hit her like a blow to the solar plexus, making her gasp as she considered the possibilities. If anybody had ever told her *not* to paint, she would have defied them, gone her own way regardless—perhaps she wasn't as nice a person as she'd thought. Not that she yelled or shouted—surely that was a good point?

'Certainly not!' She repeated it to reassure herself. 'My husband, my late husband,' this was accompanied by a freezing look, 'was a kind, understanding man—a reasonable man—unlike some I could mention,' she added stingingly but the dart bounced off his armour of conceit.

'By that, you mean you bullied him, I suppose.'

'I've never bullied anybody,' she answered him loftily. 'Like anybody else, I like doing my own thing but I've never bullied anybody to get my own way.'

'No.' He reached for her hands and drew her to her feet. 'You probably became determined, implacable and changed the subject—you don't have this for nothing,' he tapped her small, firm chin, 'and remember, I've seen you do just that. Your eyes go blank as though you're living in another world and you talk about something else.'

He was right of course, it was what she'd done when Judy had remonstrated about her coming here but, she excused herself—she and Judy were old friends, they understood each other. Herself, she didn't trespass on private ground and Judy returned the compliment. That was different—not bullying but being a private person.

'And that's wrong?' she lifted an eyebrow and almost sneered. 'To have a "keep off the grass" sign?'

'It only works when people obey the sign,' he was grave. 'Now me, I *like* to walk on grass and I'm as implacable as you are. I also like to have my own way and I've been having it for a lot longer than you so you could say it's become a habit.'

'Break it,' she advised sullenly. 'I'm going to Rome tomorrow morning.'

'No, you are not.'

'Try and stop me.' She lifted her chin.

'Already, I have,' he sighed. 'Your car is locked up in a garage to which only I have the key— nobody here will take you further than the gates— there is no public transport nearer than the village, a nine-kilometre walk, and the daily bus only goes to Grosseto but what is worse, I've stolen all your money and your passport. Now scream with frustration and kick my shins!'

Claudia felt like it but she crowded down the almost insuperable desire to do as he suggested. Instead she stood very still and descended to bad language.

'You're a low, sneaking bastard!' It only made him laugh!

'The first resort of an impotent bully—calling people names but of course, you're tired. Perhaps after a good night's sleep you'll think of something more constructive?'

'You dare to call me a bully!' The implications of what he'd said were sinking in and her eyes flicked from side to side like those of a hunted animal while, with the tip of her tongue, she licked lips suddenly gone dry. This wasn't a joke, she stole a glance up at his face—the oblique, dark eyes were hooded and the beautiful mouth was uncompromising—but he *couldn't* be serious. . . .

'You gave me the idea yourself.' He seemed able to pick up her thoughts and it made her even more uncomfortable—she felt trapped. 'I brought you here this afternoon—at least, I persuaded you to bring me. . . .'

'You tricked me into bringing you,' Claudia corrected almost automatically as her mind went round in ever decreasing circles, trying to find a way out.

'So, I tricked you,' he shrugged. 'Does it matter? I wished to delay your departure because. . . .'

'Because what?

'Because, whatever you think, we hadn't finished and I can't spare the time, at the moment, to chase you all over Europe. Unfortunately, Mama's arrival complicated things so I had to move more swiftly than I'd intended. I meant us to have just a few days together so that we could discover whether whatever is between us is worth having.' Again he shrugged. 'If it's a purely physical thing, then we could have got it out of our systems but if, as I think, there's more to it than that, we need time together. . . .'

Claudia made up her mind swiftly. Her nice, new nose thinned with temper but that was the only sign that she wasn't in complete control of the situation. 'Purely physical,' she drawled. 'It's been a long time, I suppose you could sense that. Let's go to bed!'

'Without any of the usual preliminaries?' He raised a mocking eyebrow.

'Oh those!' She hesitated slightly, found a bit of courage and went on as if this sort of conversation was an everyday thing and she wasn't feeling sick to her stomach. 'I like to get this sort of thing over as soon as possible. To be quite frank, it isn't a very important part of my life.' She remembered a phrase she'd heard in an American movie. 'Cold turkey,' she explained with considerable aplomb.

'Stop it, Claudia.' He gave her a shake which rattled her teeth. 'It isn't, hasn't ever been a part of your life—you don't know anything about it so stop behaving like a prostitute—and you're not doing that very well either. Those ladies give value for money, their customers pay for pleasure and they give it. Besides, it's too late for anything as simple as that, much as I'd like to accept your offer. Mama wouldn't approve although she'd possibly understand. So, we'll content ourselves with a few of those preliminaries you so despise and then I'll escort you to your room but only as far as the door. No, don't struggle,' as she made a desperate movement to twist her body away from him. 'Look at me, *cara*!'

Hypnosis, she decided on a spurt of hysteria as she raised her eyes to his. Dear lord, this was more or less what she'd planned, she must have been the most arrant fool to think she could handle it, she was up against a master of the craft. Dark eyes welcomed her in, strong fingers touched her gently, stroking, soothing and that damn heat was back again, uncoiling itself inside her and turning her legs to water so that she had to cling to him to stay upright.

The whole world drifted away as his face came nearer to hers, his mouth, featherlight, touched at her eyes—a silly thought obtruded and she found herself hoping her mascara tasted nice and then, his mouth was on her own and there was no more time for thinking, only feeling as her lips parted involuntarily under his.

How she got on to the couch, a couple of cushions beneath her head and him lying close against her, she didn't know—and she didn't care. There was a world of delight in his arms and his mouth and hands were promising heaven—so stupid to be afraid and clothes were such a nuisance. Her breasts were straining against the scraps of lace and silk which confined them beneath the linen shift and it was a sweet relief when he moved his hands to cup them. . . .

'Enough.' He sat up swiftly, half raising her with him until she loosened her grasp on his shoulders. '*Cara*, we've gone far beyond the bounds of what's permissible for an engaged couple, besides you've been under strain this evening—the whole day in fact and you're tired. Off to bed with you!' and he pulled her to her feet and slapped gently at her rear.

Claudia came down off the heights, nearly drowned in the cold waters of practicality but came to the surface fighting—she surprised herself.

'Purely physical,' she said it as if she was a juror giving a verdict. 'Nothing noble involved. I'm sure we needn't bother about it overmuch,' and with a very straight back, she marched out of the room without a backward glance.

Once outside and with the door closed behind her, she forced herself to walk slowly towards the stairs. The floor was tiled and her high heels would click against it so that, if she hurried, ran as she wanted to, he'd hear and she could just imagine the smile of self-satisfied knowledge on his face. Small, steady clicks as she controlled herself, made her shaking legs obey her and she was at the bottom of the staircase—more bloody marble, hadn't anybody thought about being modern and covering the damn things with carpet? But there was a way round that and she slipped her feet out of her shoes, grabbed them up and scaled the stairs as though the devil was at her heels.

And cold showers weren't all they were bragged up to be, she shivered under the icy torrent which stung her back. They did no good at all and she stumbled round the unfamiliar bedroom, knocking herself against the heavy, old-fashioned furniture as she slid her shivering body into a nightie, slapped a bit of cream on her face and tumbled into bed convinced she wouldn't sleep a wink because no matter how cold she was on the outside, the heat was still within her making her twist and turn. She wanted, oh yes, she wanted! Wanted his arms round her, his hands touching, the weight of him on her and a lot of other things she could only guess at.

Viciously, she bit at the lace-trimmed sheet and hoped he was having as bad a time as she was!

Claudia threw down her paintbrush with a lot less than her usual care and it rolled gently across the grass leaving a trail of cadmium yellow in its wake. For two days, she'd practically been confined to barracks. Nicolo had been away, heaven knew where, he hadn't thought her important enough to be told, she supposed. She, his *fidanzata* had been abandoned without a word, even a 'goodbye, see you some time' and his mother had taken over as wardress! Dear Claudia mustn't exert herself, that was the drill so, without her transport—the Allegro was still locked in the garage—and with nothing else to do, she'd listened while the signora had been voluble on her favourite subject, Venice. Claudia had been there once and painted a charming scene of several mooring posts and a gondola complete with a tenor gondolier, all against the background of a flaming sunset.

She was grateful for that painting, it had started her off in the reproduction business—reproduced on textured board and framed cheaply but tastefully in white and gold plastic, it had sold by the hundreds and had earned her quite a reputation. It had even been exported so she ought to be grateful to Venice—but not grateful enough to have the place rammed down her throat *ad infinitum*.

So, on this third day, Nicolo still being absent, she had collected her easel, her canvas stool and hunted for a subject, finding a charming fountain in a secluded corner of the extensive gardens which made a good focal point amid the flowers and low hedges of myrtle. She'd worked hard at it all morning and the result was ghastly. It looked as though she was unable even to draw a straight line!

But there had been interruptions—Emilia kept sending a little maid with jugs of lemon or lime juice, plates containing substantial servings of pizza or little cakes made of honey and nuts—the juice was welcome but the food was not and finally, the signora had come, suggesting that a canal scene with St Mark's in the background would have more appeal so the *luna di miele* ought, naturally to be spent in Venice at the signora's own house which she would vacate immediately in order that it might be freshened up for the happy couple.

Claudia retrieved the paint brush and guiltily wiped up as much of the cadmium yellow as possible although she wasn't happy about what she suspected turpentine might do to the emerald green, smoothly shaven grass of the lawn. She was just debating whether to mix up a load of green and paint over the stained grass when a light tenor voice spoke from behind her.

'Yes, signorina, I think I understand what you are trying to say.'

Claudia went rigid with disapproval. She hadn't been trying to 'say' anything—she left things like that to the real artists—the ones who would starve before they painted things like her pot boilers—a camera would have done the job just as well except that a camera couldn't transfer a tree from where it was growing to another position where it would add balance to the scene. With a disgusted little snort, she pulled her straw hat more firmly on to her head and tugged at the brim.

'Thank you, signor, an appreciative audience is all I need!' On a par with the pizza and cakes, she could have added—unwelcome! And she swung round on her stool to have a good look at her critic and what she saw made her lips curve in sardonic appreciation.

Her critic was about her own age, a strikingly good-looking young man with the kind of good looks expected of young Italians. A lot of shiningly glossy black, wavy hair, a smooth, olive-tinted complexion, sparkling white teeth and dark lustrous eyes in an almost perfectly shaped face—Rudolph Valentino brought up to date. She bet the nostrils of his aristocratic nose would thin with barely controlled passion when he was murmuring sweet nothings in some very rich young lady's ear.

And he was a little too well dressed as well as being too good looking—his navy silk jacket had a waist which was a little too tight, his trousers were just that much too sharply creased—one could cut one's fingers on those edges—and the silk cravat about his neck was ever so slightly too colourful against the white of his open-necked shirt. Added to which, he was wearing the latest thing in two-tone shoes. Mentally, she contrasted him with Nicolo and he fell by the wayside.

'I'm always glad of a critic,' she informed him dulcetly. 'One can learn so much from the observations of an impartial observer, especially a stranger.'

'*Molte grazie*, signora.' White, very even teeth flashed in a charming smile and then he looked rueful. 'There is nobody to introduce us properly but I am Alessandro Gabrielli and you must be Signora Currey and since we are to be relatives, we don't have to be so very formal, do we?'

'Not a bit,' Claudia said cheerfully. 'I don't bother with formality myself but—how did you know?'

'Call me Sandro.' Once more the smile flashed, sweet and urchinlike. 'The papers, signora—Zio Nicolo—now, he *is* formal—the announcement was in yesterday's editions so I came at once to offer my good wishes and to meet the lady who is going to be my *zia*. A new experience for me, I've never had one before.' The dark, lustrous eyes filled with sadness, he looked bereft. 'My mother died when I was only three years old—so—picture me, a lonely little boy without any softening feminine influence at all.'

'How terrible for you,' Claudia said it but she didn't mean it. This young man didn't strike her as a victim of deprivation and she certainly wasn't going to offer to mother him, she wasn't old enough. She looked at her painting and with a sigh of regret for a wasted morning, she commenced to pack up her gear. Perhaps she'd have better luck in the afternoon or, better still, the evening—a softer light, longer shadows might make the fountain look mysterious and romantic. She started to visualise the scene and unaccountably it changed to one of moonlight where the green stains on the mouths of the water-spouting dolphins became leprous looking—the shadowed cracks in the masonry blocks were crooked and emphasised, so that the whole edifice looked old and diseased and, of course, the trees would crowd round it—not romantic at all but decadent and macabre.

With a little sigh, she turned away. Her trouble was that she had an outsized imagination. 'No, leave it,' she told Sandro as he stooped to gather up her easel and other bits and pieces. 'I'll come back later when the light's softer—it's too blindingly harsh in the morning. Are you staying long?'

Sandro gave her a smile which was wryly comical. 'I—er—hope to be invited to stay the night. I don't hope for much more than that! Zio Nicolo is not always hospitable,' he became rather melancholy. 'A family matter, you understand. Would you like me to explain?'

He was going to explain whether she liked or not so she nodded perfunctorily to save time. 'My grandfather married twice, you know,' he continued, the air of melancholy deepening. 'The first wife was of the nobility, a contessa but alas, not rich. She was my grandmother and her son, my father, also married into a noble family but again, a lady with no money. Love matches both but it needed more than love to support the Villa Gabrielli. Fortunately, my grandfather's second marriage was to a Venetian lady who was very wealthy although less well bred—Zio Nicolo is her son and when my father died—the death of my mother took away his will to live—I had this place and no money so Zio Nicolo bought it from me and I sometimes think he is a little jealous that I am head of the family. Myself, I am grateful that my house remains in the hands of a Gabrielli—I am not bitter at all, but as I said, I think Zio

Nicolo often feels like a usurper so, to spare his feelings, I don't come here very often. You will understand, signora, how a little envy can warp a man's judgment.'

'Oh yes,' and Claudia thought she did but she wasn't sure if they were talking about the same man being warped. She'd seen no signs of it in Nicolo—admittedly he was an overbearing swine who thought he always knew best but at worst, she'd never thought of him in connection with anything as futile and trivial as envy—he was much too sure of himself. But this young man—that was a different matter. Oh well, it was none of her business and she sought desperately to change the subject.

'I'm sure you will be made very welcome,' she informed him chattily. 'Signora Gabrielli is staying here, she arrived three, or was it four days ago. . . .'

'Nonna Venetia,' from under the brim of her hat, she watched him make a little moué which disappeared almost as soon as it was born to leave his dark eyes lustrous and appealing and his mouth curved into a sweet smile.

'And,' she added, 'Nicolo is away at the moment and nobody seems to know when he'll be back or even where he's gone.' Sandro seemed a pleasant enough young man, she thought but she couldn't quite squash down the feeling that he was a bit indiscreet—although perhaps Italians were more forthcoming than English people. She couldn't imagine anybody she knew at home revealing strictly family matters to what amounted to a stranger even if that stranger was engaged to be married to a relative!

Emilia had been at it again! When they reached

the terrace, the lunch table was set for four and Signora Gabrielli was drifting towards it, dressed in floating, watery green silk and pearls—in which she looked well bred enough to take her place anywhere. The faded gold of her abundant hair was drawn back smoothly, in deep waves to a skilfully constructed chignon and her narrow feet were shod in pale green kid with a modest heel.

Claudia looked down at herself, at her paint-stained smock, her old, faded and paint-stained jeans and at the crumbling rubber flip flops on her bare feet before she smiled ruefully.

'I'm not fit to be seen,' she murmured, 'much less join you at the lunch table.' She glanced at the fourth place setting and raised her eyebrows. 'You've heard from Nicolo? Will he be here to lunch?'

'So Emilia informs me.' The Signora gave a wide smile and turned her attention to Sandro. 'You and I shall have a little chat while Claudia makes herself respectable. It's a long time since I last saw you, Sandro—four or five years, I think so you must tell me all about Rome and how many hearts you've broken there—Violetta delli Capretti, for instance. . . .'

'The ladies of Venice are great gossips, Claudia,' Sandro smiled engagingly. 'You would think the news of my little romance wouldn't travel so far— Rome to Venice but Nonna Venetia knows all about it,' his look was rueful. 'Even that it's over!'

'What else did you expect?' the signora snorted elegantly before she turned on Claudia. 'Off with you, child and make yourself respectable. Stains, I can bear—even jeans and bare feet but you smell like a paint factory. And while you're making yourself presentable, I shall give my grandson a list of young ladies, any one of whom would make

him a much better wife than the little Violetta—
the girl was well enough but her mother . . .!'

And Claudia went off to her room chuckling at
the wryly humorous face Sandro had made at her
behind the signora's back and at the signora's
craftiness. Nicolo's mother hadn't known the
romance was over—she'd called the girl a milk-
and-water little ninny and expected a marriage but
she'd covered her surprise well—a formidable
lady!

Half an hour later she returned to the terrace,
shining with cleanliness and smelling nicely of
Vetyver by Lanvin—which she had splashed
generously over herself, preferring its astringency
to the other flowery perfumes. She was wearing
another of Maris' cast-offs, a skirt and top in
white, very simple and unfussy—as were all of her
cousin's designs—the only decoration being one
bold diagonal stripe of luminescent green across
the front of the top. And, since Nicolo was
obviously expected—and she suspected he'd make
a fuss if it was missing—the turquoise and pearl
ring adorned her finger again.

'Much better!' His mother beamed at her and
patted the seat of a nearby chair while Sandro's
eyes expressed admiration subtly. Emilia was
bustling to and fro, chivvying a little maid and
everybody was waiting, waiting for the master to
arrive. Claudia said it to herself and nearly burst
into laughter, it sounded so damn Victorian.
Below the terrace, on the drive, she could see the
big, black car—a Chevrolet, she'd learned—so
Nicolo must be about somewhere and while she
listened with half an ear to the conversation
between the signora and Sandro, she mentally
fortified herself for the encounter.

He'd won all the previous battles, especially the last one on the night of the engagement party, but she was determined he shouldn't win any more. The thing to do was to be completely relaxed and gently humorous, she told herself—humour was death to romance—she'd heard that somewhere—but not too relaxed! Or she'd find herself taken over and turned into a mindless twit. What was she worrying about anyway? He could hardly do or say anything in front of his mother and Sandro.

Which gave her an idea and she turned a charming smile on Nicolo's nephew, let her eyes go soft and dreamy as she inspected his almost too good-looking face and felt a momentary triumph as he responded instantly with a languishing glance from his large dark, thickly lashed eyes.

'Nicolo's arrived?' She made it a half question to his mother and at the answering nod, 'Good, I've just realised how hungry I am. I hope he won't be long.'

CHAPTER SIX

LUNCH was served the minute that Nicolo set foot out on the terrace and he didn't keep them waiting long. His behaviour was impeccable, he kissed his mother's fingers, he kissed Claudia's and greeted his nephew without any signs of hostility but Claudia thought she detected a faint withdrawal as though he had erected a 'Keep off the Grass' sign. For her sake, Claudia supposed, the conversation was kept in English although Sandro lapsed into Italian once or twice. If anybody was to blame for hostility, she decided, it was Sandro, who had decided to flirt delicately with her and Claudia, after one swift, defiant glare at her *fidanzato*, flirted back for all she was worth, feeling an arid sort of triumph as she glanced at Nicolo and saw his mouth becoming no longer beautiful but rather grim and forbidding.

But these were only small signs, outwardly they were all the best of friends and it wasn't until the meal finally ended and the signora had beguiled Sandro into accompanying her on a stroll in the gardens that the peace and friendliness splintered into fragments and Claudia found herself attempting to cope with a very angry man.

'You will behave yourself.' Emilia had superintended the clearing of the table and they were quite alone but he bit the words out in a savage undertone.

'I always do,' she murmured gently. 'It's a habit. I can remember my mother—she always said I must behave myself and after a while, it became standard practice. A lesson well learned,' she continued aggravatingly as she watched his eyes narrow, 'and one I've been following ever since we met—otherwise I'd have spat in your eye long ago!' She wasn't coping very well. Ideally, she supposed she should have tried to smooth him down, but at least she was keeping her end up and then his soft laugh surprised her so that she looked again at his face, and found he was smiling as though he was enjoying the encounter and his dark, oblique eyes were warmly understanding.

'Sandro's too young for you, *cara*,' he mocked. 'He's only in it for the money and where there isn't any money, he accepts the fringe benefits and goes on his way. You should know that.'

'Having only just met him and knowing nothing about him,' she mocked back, 'I hesitate to make such a sweeping judgment,' and as a shuttered look passed over his face. 'Have I said something wrong?'

'No.' The shuttered look vanished and his eyes twinkled. 'You've only demonstrated that you're a babe in arms, an innocent at large. I'm a very lucky man.'

'You'll regret it,' she cooed softly while her hazel eyes, turned very green with anger, raged at him and then, with a quick glance round to see nobody was within earshot, 'How long does this little act have to go on? I mean, I understand about your mother, I wouldn't upset her for the world but when will she be going back to Venice?'

'Not until she sees us safely married, *cara*,' he sounded amused. 'Somehow, you've managed to convince her you'll make me the perfect wife.'

'Oh, I would,' she agreed charmingly, 'but that's

To Susan Welland
Mills & Boon
Reader Service
FREEPOST
P.O. Box 236
CROYDON
Surrey CR9 9EL.

SEND NO MONEY NOW

FREE BOOKS CERTIFICATE

Dear Susan,

Your special Introductory Offer of 12 Free books is too good to miss. I understand they are mine to keep with the Free Tote Bag.

Please also reserve a Reader Service Subscription for me. If I decide to subscribe, I shall, from the beginning of the month following my free parcel of books, receive 12 new books each month for £13.20, post and packing free. If I decide not to subscribe, I shall write to you within 10 days. The free books will be mine to keep, in any case.

I understand that I may cancel my subscription at any time simply by writing to you. I am over 18 years of age.

2R5TT

Name _____ Signature _____
(BLOCK CAPITALS PLEASE)
Address _____

_____ Postcode _____

Open your heart to Love
with 12 Romances Free
your welcome gift from Mills & Boon

Love, romance, intrigue...all are captured for you by Mills & Boon's top selling authors. By becoming a regular reader of Mills & Boon's romances you can enjoy twelve superb new titles every month plus a whole range of special benefits: your very own personal membership card, a free monthly newsletter packed with recipes, competitions, exclusive book offers and a monthly guide to the stars, plus extra bargain offers and big cash savings.

As a special introduction we will send you 12 exciting Mills & Boon Romances and an exclusive Mills & Boon Tote Bag FREE when you complete and return this card.

At the same time we will reserve a subscription to Mills & Boon Reader Service for you. Every month, you will receive twelve of the very latest novels by leading Romantic Fiction authors, delivered direct to your door. And they cost just the same as they would in the shops – postage and packing is always completely Free. There is no obligation or commitment – you can cancel your subscription at any time.

It's so easy! Send no money now – you don't even need a stamp. Just fill in and detach this card and send it off today.

ROMANCE
Pacific Aphrodite
MADELINE KER

ROMANCE
The Silver Flame

Come Love

plus the exclusive
Mills & Boon
TOTE BAG
FREE

by the way. The point in question is whether I think you'd make me the perfect husband and I don't think you would—a satisfying husband, if you like but not a satisfactory one.'

'Both satisfying and satisfactory as you'll admit one day,' his answer came swiftly. 'Claudia, my dear, I've worked out your reason for coming here—and don't try to put me off with tales of painting pictures because we both know that's a lie—you came, shall we say to be revenged on the Gabriellis for what they did to you, for causing the death of your husband and your cousin. . . .'

'Just one Gabrielli.' She lifted her eyes and looked straight into his, very calm and as cold as ice although her heart had lurched with a strange fear as he'd said it. 'But I've discarded the idea. It kept me going when I was in hospital, gave me something to live for, but now it sounds too melodramatic for words. I just want to get back to England and start all over again from scratch. I want to put everything behind me, make a new beginning. . . .'

'Which is what I'm offering,' he pointed out. 'A new beginning and I'm not only offering, I'm insisting. In any case, what you were contemplating would have been very dangerous, I'm glad you're no longer of the same mind. We can work something out between us now, something better than a simple physical relationship. . . .' And all the time he was talking, his eyes were beckoning. Personal magnetism, she found herself thinking and she wasn't resisting—she couldn't resist. If only somebody would come along, his mother, Emilia, even the little maid, anybody to interrupt, to release her—and he wasn't even touching her!

It was like being on a slippery slope, knowing

she was going to slip and start to slide and knowing as well that once started, she'd not be able to stop. Come on in, the water's wonderful! But it was also deep, too deep for her and there could be a current in there which was too strong, which would sweep her away. With an enormous effort, she pulled herself together before she could start sliding, gulped—a gulp which she turned into a polite little cough and tried to be sensible. A man she'd known for only a few weeks—a man who had captivated Maris—well that was an excuse if ever she needed one—a man would have to be really something to turn Maris' head. . . .

'What do you suggest?' she heard herself say it and could hardly believe her ears.

'I suggest we please Mama, she can hardly wait to dandle a baby on her knee and I've attended to the formalities. We can be married in about three weeks' time.' The battle over, he leaned back in his chair and lit a cigarette with a satisfied air which demolished her acquiescence so that she could take a second breath and come out fighting.

'What a reason for getting married,' she snorted. 'To please your mama!'

'It'll do for a beginning,' he was grave. 'Later on, I'll teach you a few other reasons which have nothing to do with the wishes of my mother.' His hand closed over hers and she felt the warm strength of his fingers as they clasped her own. 'You wished to go to Rome, you shall go—you and Mama. She makes an orgy of shopping and you've a lot to buy. My mother has excellent taste and she'll help you choose your wedding dress and the rest of the things you'll need. She's looking forward to it.'

Rome, the name sounded in her head like a bell.

With or without his mother, once in Rome she could count herself as good as free—if she had transport. She would have to be careful of the signora's heart condition but in Rome, away from him, she'd be able to think and plan once more—stop being a mindless zombie—get back to arranging her own life instead of having everything done for her.

'I could drive your mother down in the Allegro,' she mused aloud. 'I know we wouldn't want to use it in Rome, not for getting about—taxis are so much more convenient but it would be useful on the journey back, there's so much room in it—as good as an estate any day. We could stay in a nice hotel, central for the shops. . . .'

'Mama's very fond of the Villa Medici above the Spanish Steps,' he murmured, eyes sparkling wickedly, 'and she usually patronises Ungaro in the Via Borgognona. . . .'

'Oh no!' Claudia came out of her fog of ifs and perhaps to land with a bump in cold practicality. 'That's for the jet setters and I couldn't afford anything as expensive as that.' But if she was pushed, she could—it all depended on how long the signora intended to stay in Rome—that and how long it would take her, Claudia, to think up a good reason for not returning with Nicolo's mama.

Then, she could go to the apartment—thank heaven Maris' *avvocato* had persuaded her not to sell it—she could hide there until it was convenient to start back to England. The place hadn't been lived in for two years but she didn't suppose it would be damp—and if Nicolo went looking for her, he'd never think of Rome—she hoped! But perhaps he wouldn't—good riddance to bad rubbish and all that. But she was surprised at the sadness she felt when she thought of him giving up so easily—cheered in one way and bitterly disappointed in another—quite illogical.

'You said you would paint this afternoon, Claudia.' Sandro came up the steps to the terrace alone and with only the briefest explanation to his uncle. 'Nonna Venetia has gone to her room for the siesta, Zio, so I thought I would watch Claudia paint.'

'Painting?' He raised an eyebrow at her.

'The fountain,' she answered sweetly, 'since I'm discouraged from going further afield to find a subject, I tried it this morning but I wasn't in the mood. It was there Sandro found me just as I'd thrown down my brush in disgust.'

'Ah, but Claudia,' Sandro melted with concern, 'Zio Nicolo wouldn't understand the artistic temperament, he is a mere business man. Show him a set of accounts and he is concerned only if they show a loss and even then, he wouldn't throw down his calculator in disgust, as you say. He would send for the auditors, have it all checked and then sell the company or close it down.'

'Just as I thought,' she mourned. 'Your uncle has no soul, Sandro.' This light, frothy type of conversation was just what she needed, it needed no concentration and she didn't have to examine every word before she let it slip from her lips. 'Come and sit by me while I try again,' she suggested. 'Make me laugh. I don't seem to have been doing much of that lately.'

'I am yours to command,' Sandro grinned engagingly from where he stood behind Nicolo and Claudia, not to be outdone, smiled back at him over the top of her *fidanzato*'s head.

'Quite impossible!' That was the *fidanzato* being brusque and from under her lowered lids, she watched their faces. Nicolo's wore an implacable look, she could almost tell what he was thinking. Things were going to go *his* way or they wouldn't go at all! And then her glance slid up to Sandro and her heart gave a little thump of shock but only momentarily, the expression of utter rage which had so briefly contorted his good-looking face was gone almost before she could identify it and he was once more his smiling, handsome self. Sternly, she told herself it had been her imagination—she had expected him to show some emotion at Nicolo's flat statement, so she had conjured up an expression in her mind—that was all it was.

'I see Sandro so seldom.' That was Nicolo being quietly emphatic. 'And since he's here, there are several matters we have to discuss, but it shouldn't take more than a couple of hours. . . .' He was actually relenting and Claudia sustained another shock—that he could!

'You see how it is, Claudia,' Sandro smiled wryly. 'Didn't I tell you that my zio wasn't very hospitable but I think his main trouble is jealousy, don't you?' The amusement in his voice and his impish smile robbed the words of any offence and they certainly seemed to have little effect on his uncle—Nicolo's features held neither anger nor irritation. 'He's afraid I shall steal you from him,' Sandro went on explaining, 'and who could blame me if I tried? You are so very beautiful, so young and anybody can see that my zio is much too old for you. What is it you English say—one foot in the grave?'

Claudia felt colour sweeping up to her face, a hot embarrassment which she was unable to control at such an exhibition of childish, almost spiteful impudence but her face was shaded by a rioting bougainvillaea which sprawled abandonedly over the pillars which supported the roof of the terrace and her voice—when she found it—was coolly amused.

'Far from it.' She forced a small chuckle and hoped it sounded as mirthful as she intended. 'Your uncle isn't a bit too old for me, he's a very nice age, an interesting age.' She would have liked to add that Nicolo—praise god—was long past behaving childishly, if he'd ever been childish— which she didn't think he had. He seemed to her to be one of those people who went from boyhood to instant maturity.

On impulse, she stood up, walked across to him and planted a kiss straight on his unsuspecting mouth, the mouth responded instantly and a firm hand clasped at the nape of her neck to hold her face to his. When she was allowed to raise her head, very dark brown eyes looked straight into hers and the message was that he appreciated the gesture although it was quite unnecessary and she gave him a little nod as if to say, 'I know but. . . .' If somebody had suggested she had acted out of either love or loyalty, she would have denied it hotly—love didn't come into it and she had no reason to be loyal to him, she'd done it only to put Sandro in his place.

'You see,' she turned to Sandro with a wide smile and then back to Nicolo with an ominous glint in her eyes, 'your uncle has no need to be jealous of anybody, Sandro. He knows *exactly* what I feel about him!' and she wandered off in the direction of the fountain, feeling very pleased with herself.

The original pencil sketch she had made of the fountain was good, she decided, but it could be improved if she eliminated a lot of the myrtle hedge and replaced it with a couple of nicely positioned junipers—the dark, needle-like shapes would offset the pale bulk of the fountain admirably. She spent a busy hour, sheets of white paper cascading around her until at last she was satisfied and set up a new, clean board on the easel. Without looking—her box of paints was always arranged in the same way—she reached for a tube which she always used for the initial wash, squeezed some on to her palette and found it was cobalt blue.

It annoyed her and she swore briefly as she dropped the tube back into its alloted space, only to find that occupied by something else. A moment's glance was sufficient to tell her that everything was jumbled and she swore again, this time at herself for being so stupid—and yet, when it came to the tools of her trade, she didn't make mistakes like that—never had—not even when she'd restarted painting after James' death. She'd always prided herself on her organisation—Lord! Nicolo *must* be getting to her to make her break the habits of years in this way.

Fiercely, she concentrated on getting her box back in order and then on getting an outline down on the board—a whole hour wasted and she was irritable when Nicolo's tread came on the grass behind her and a mocking, 'You haven't done much, I believe you've been asleep.'

'I don't want any interruptions please,' she was surly. 'Go away, find some other poor woman to harry, I'm busy and I can't be bothered with an audience.'

'And you're not wearing your ring,' he pointed out, ignoring her grumbles.

'In the box with the chinese white,' she threw the words over her shoulder. 'I don't when I'm working, turps *can't* be good for it, the setting, you know and all those little seed pearls and turquoises. It would be a pity to spoil it.' And to save further speech, she rammed the thick brush, with which she was reddening the zinnias, between her teeth and reached for a thinner one.

Both brushes were taken away from her, the one in her hand gently, but when she clenched her jaws on the one between her teeth, he prised her mouth apart with two fingers and extracted it forcibly.

'I could have got splinters in my tongue, you doing that,' she raged. 'Honestly, there's no peace in this place—not only do I have to paint things which are only fit for birthday cards. . . .'

'This would go on a birthday card?'

'Most of my failures do,' she was sardonic and shrugged. 'I have to earn my living any way I can and my agent usually manages to place my work—greetings cards if it's not fit for framing. I think this one will do nicely for an anniversary card, don't you?—bring back memories of a honeymoon, very romantic—perhaps I'd better do it by moonlight!'

'And after we're married, you'll still go on painting?'

'If we're married,' she corrected. 'Oh, I know you've made all the arrangements but nobody's bothered to ask me if it's what I want,' and then she remembered about the trip to Rome. Now, that was a thing she did want.

Maybe she'd get there and miss him so much she'd come straight back without making any attempt to escape. Why, oh why hadn't he run true to form—suggested she become his mistress instead of doing the thing properly and talking about marriage? The one she could have dismissed out of hand but the latter, especially as it seemed he wasn't taking no for an answer and wasn't above several underhand tricks to get his own way—thoughts of the latter were beginning to bring her out in a cold sweat. And it had nothing to do with memories of James, she was over that period of her life— she still had a sweet nostalgia about it, but it all seemed such a long time ago, almost a dream—a sweet memory but no more than that.

'The point is, that when it comes to my life and what I do with it, I like to be consulted occasionally,' she snarled belligerently.

'Then we shall have our first consultation.' He reached into the pocket of his jacket and extracted a small jeweller's box. 'Do you think turps might spoil this one?'

Reluctantly, she opened the box and blinked at magnificence. 'Oh, a cubic zirconia! I've always wanted one of those.'

'And you very well know it's no such thing,' he reproved as he slid it on her finger.

'If it isn't,' she sniffed, 'it's positively vulgar. A cubic zirconia, I could accept but this! I wouldn't feel safe except in a bank vault.'

'But it will match the suite you and Mama are going to occupy in the Villa Medici,' Nicolo's mouth curved into a smile but the firmness of it didn't diminish by one iota. 'And I think there's more to this small ceremony than you saying "thank you", which you haven't done yet.'

'Remiss of me,' Claudia was back to normal,

cool and composed. 'Remind me to look it up in my book on etiquette. I think—but I'm not sure—that I ought to faint or something.'

'Of the two, I think I prefer the "or something".' He had pulled her to her feet and into his arms. 'There's nothing very exciting about a fainting woman.'

'You're very sure of yourself.' She tried hard to make it a sneer but it came out as a husky murmur which, to her own ears sounded vaguely inviting.

'Of course,' he admitted serenely. 'I'm always sure of myself, which is why I've decided to hurry things along. I'd have a grey beard down to my knees if I waited for you to make up your mind. Such a tortuous mind, full of ideas which make very little sense. Be sensible, *cara*, leave the decisions to me. I assure you I know very well what you want—better than you do and—you still haven't said "thank you". If you'll lift up your face, I'll show you how I like to be thanked.'

'I'm being run over by a steamroller,' she protested but the protest was silenced when his mouth came on hers and her last practical thought was that there weren't any colours in her box to paint a sky as blue as the one above her, nor reproduce the green of the grass. Every colour was enhanced and the soft droning of a bee became inexplicably loud until she realised it wasn't a bee but the blood thrumming in her ears.

Her eyes drifted shut while a strange wildness took possession of her, driving her to cling to him, to fondle his ears and thread her fingers through his hair, rumpling the guinea gold waves into curls while her mouth parted beneath his so that the tip of his tongue caressed the softness and his hands were stroking and soothing everywhere—soothing?

She almost sobbed against his lips. She'd been kissed before but not like this.

'And that is how I like to be thanked.' Nicolo raised his head although he still kept a firm grasp on her and thank heaven for that, she thought muzzily. Without that firm hold, she would have slid down because her legs refused to hold her.

'At least,' he continued smoothly, 'it will do for the present. Later, you'll learn other ways of thanking me. Did I please you?'

'Out of a wealth of experience, I'll bet,' she muttered and watched as oblique, dark eyes drooped in mock modesty.

'Most men have experience, *cara*,' he almost whispered it, 'and I am no exception. I have—er—some—no more and no less than any other man, I suppose. You object?'

Nicolo didn't give her a chance to say either yea or nay, he put a finger under her chin, tilting her face up so that he could look into her eyes under the hat brim. 'It's very potent, isn't it—this thing between us and you're afraid of it. I think you feel it may be a loss of identity, hmm?'

It gave her a chance to recover and she bounced back like a rubber ball. 'Oh, for heaven's sake, don't go into the Freudian bit! It's what you said it was, purely physical—there's nothing mind bending about it. I daresay any other man would do—old Mother Nature having her way.'

'But don't you let me catch you experimenting.' The warning was accompanied by a little shake. 'Perhaps this short stay in Rome isn't such a good idea. . . .'

'But your mother will be with me,' she reminded him, acidly sweet.

'But she can't watch you every minute of the

day and night,' the finger left her chin and he pulled her down to sit on the grass beside him. 'Perhaps I should come with you. . . .'

'Oh no!' Claudia could see her avenue of escape closing before her eyes. If he came, it would be the Chevrolet—they'd all go together—the Allegro would stay locked up in the garage—flight would be impossible. She *needed* her little car—'Fittings and things,' she tempered her vehemence with sweet reason. 'A man would be in the way and you'd be dreadfully bored—men always are at that sort of thing.'

'Intrigued would be a better word.'

'Your English is very good,' she complimented chattily. 'I don't think I've ever heard a foreigner speak it so well.'

'Certainly.' He accepted it as a compliment. 'I do most things well, if I do them at all—my English is a by product from my mother's glass factory which I manage for her.' He leaned back on the grass so that she could look down on his face and watch the few expressions he allowed himself flit over his features. 'It's a good little factory, and we have men working there who are artists, they don't make the usual tourist stuff—it would be too expensive since most of it is hand made and it's far too good to be wrapped up in the bottom of a suitcase and battered in travelling. I went looking for markets elsewhere than in Italy and found that in England there were people who appreciated our product so—I learned English properly. That was all a long time ago but I visit your country frequently, keep myself up to date with the vernacular—I find your slang and your regional accents fascinating. Each time I go, you've thought of a new way of saying something.'

'Like "no"? Now that's a word you should get a slant on.'

'But so many girls use it,' dark brown eyes looked up into hers wickedly.

'You ought to be ashamed of admitting it,' she scolded while a small cold feeling crept round her heart. 'On second thoughts, I don't think I'll marry you after all—going away so frequently—other women—Ugh! And you've the nerve to warn me about experimenting?'

'You could come with me,' he conceded, 'at least, until the children arrive—you'd have to stay with them while they're small and need you. . . .'

'Dear lord!' Claudia moved away from him on the pretext of picking up an overlooked tube of paint. 'First, a husband I don't really need, or want, for that matter and now the man's lumbering me with a load of kids! I shall make you a bad wife and I'll be an even worse mother—let's break the engagement before we start doing each other harm.'

'No,' his hand closed on her hip as she struggled on to all fours. 'I like it the way it is, so do you only you're too obstinate to admit it. . . .'

'I am *not* obstinate!'

'You are, like a little mule. . . .'

'You mean a donkey. . . .'

'No,' he was grasping a handful of blue denim and he tugged at it so that she tumbled flat beside him. 'Donkeys are very sensible, more so than horses. I said a mule and that's what I meant.' And as her teeth snapped an inch from his nose, 'You even bite!'

'Lecherous pig!' she exclaimed a few minutes later when she had struggled herself free and was rearranging her crumpled clothing.

'And you enjoyed every moment of it!' He rose to his feet in one lithe movement and held out a hand. 'Come along, my not so reluctant *fidanzata*. Mama will be waiting for us, she's had Emilia make tea for you specially.'

There wasn't a lot of time for thinking. Once back in the house, Claudia had to wash and change again—she mourned her carefree days when she could eat a scrambled together meal hurriedly, not caring whether she looked paint-stained or not. Nowadays, it seemed she did nothing but change from working clothes to presentable ones and back again at the speed of light. Wasting time—and she glowered at herself in the bathroom mirror—valuable time, painting time—time she could have put to a better use than sitting around, drinking tea and talking inanities. But the signora was as implacable as her son and the inanities were all of forward planning today.

'So much to do,' the elder lady beamed with anticipation. 'A few things for you to wear immediately. We can buy them off the peg, as you say and they will see you through until other things are made for you.'

'I can't afford a lot of anything.' Claudia, feeling like a rabbit trapped in a burrow by a determined ferret, became desperately opposed to forward planning—her firm little chin set squarely and she stared glassily into the distance. 'Clothes don't interest me very much.'

'My wedding gift,' the signora waved objections aside and Sandro chose this moment to add his mite.

'The advantage, the main advantage of a rich family, Claudia. They don't wave a magic wand, they wave a cheque book—you'll get used to it in time.' His mouth had a wry twist to it and Claudia regarded him sympathetically, becoming so lost in pity for him that she missed most of the signora's answer, only catching the end of it which was a little homily on how to spend money wisely.

'. . . and at least Claudia seems able to do that!' she finished with a definite snap but the little exchange had given Claudia a new sight of Sandro—good looking and a bit weak, put in the shade by his wealthy relatives and a bit bitter about it—she sympathised with him. He evidently disliked being treated as an object of charity as much as she, herself did.

'I shall pay for my clothes myself,' she tempered her sharpness with a smile at Nicolo's mother, 'although I'll be grateful for your advice. I've never bothered about what I wear, I don't even know what are the latest fashions so I'd appreciate your help.'

'Some interchangeable separates and a few classics,' Signora Gabrielli was still on the subject at dinner time and Claudia swiftly concealed a grin. She had as many interchangeable separates as a woman could want—a great stock of them hanging in Maris' wardrobe in Maris' apartment and although they would all be two years behind the current fashion trends, Maris had always tended towards the classical cut—and they would all fit—she and her cousin had been the same size, shape and colouring. A quick visit to the apartment—raid the wardrobe, and she'd be quite well dressed at no cost—she didn't need the Gabrielli largesse. In any case, as a last resort, she could use some of the money from the sale of Maris' boutique. So far, she'd been loth to touch it but Maris would have approved, if it was spent on clothes.

Claudia isolated herself in silence while her thoughts went on, round and round, never coming to any real conclusion. She waded through a plateful of pasta served with a strong Genoese sauce and washed away the taste with sips of Chianti. The label on the bottle said 'classico' and 'riservo' but for her, its only virtue was that it washed away the pungency of the sauce.

'It's a good wine,' Nicolo had observed her grimace of distaste. 'From our own vineyard near Florence.' Claudia nodded and went on with her thoughts.

All things considered, she was quite well off—if she needed money, she only had to see Maris' *avvocato* in Rome. Perhaps a visit to him would be wise. If Nicolo wouldn't allow her to drive the Allegro to Rome, she needn't be stranded—she could always buy another car but she was fond of the brown hatchback which tried so hard to look like an estate—she was used to it and she didn't want to replace it with something which had the steering wheel on the wrong side. Escape was the word and she preferred to escape in the Allegro.

But lying in bed that night, her thoughts took another turn. It was very nice to be pampered and cossetted, to be cared for, and when she finally went, she was going to miss it. Not that she would mind so much, she preferred to make her own decisions and it wasn't as if she was in love or anything stupid like that. One couldn't love a man one had known for only a few short weeks. One would miss him, of course but that was all.

The trouble was that for the last two years or so, she'd led the life of a nun—mostly on her own and so bound up in her own affairs, her dedication to the main object—which was to make him suffer—

that she'd practically withdrawn from life. Only—she turned restlessly in the bed before shutting her eyes firmly and willing herself to sleep. But sleep refused to come.

An hour later, she slid out of bed and crossed to the window. Below her, shining across the terrace, were the lights from the *salotto* and the scent of a cigar rising from the terrace. Without thinking too much, she looked over the rail of her balcony and called 'Hey' very softly.

'Claudia?' Nicolo was standing in a shadowy corner, well out of the stream of light from the windows and she caught the flash of his white teeth as he said her name and then the glowing arc as he tossed the cigar over on to the path.

'Can I have a word with you?' She called it softly.

'Now?'

'Yes, right now.'

'Then come down, or would you prefer me to come up?'

'I'll come down,' and swiftly, she stepped back into the room, slid herself out of her nightie and struggled into jeans and a top—once she'd got the matter of the Allegro sorted out, she would be able to sleep—and on bare feet, she pattered out into the corridor and down the stairs.

CHAPTER SEVEN

NICOLO was waiting for her in the *salotto*. The two big crystal chandeliers which had lit the room had been switched off and only one standard lamp, the light softened by a big parchment shade, cast a pool of diffused light over a couch which stood by the fireplace. Nicolo was straightening up from thrusting a burning taper among the kindling under some logs when she crept in. His stern face relaxed into a smile when he saw her, but his eyebrows were raised in a question.

Claudia looked round at the rest of the huge room, at the shadowy shapes of chairs, tables and couches—at the gleam where gilded frames picked up the light from the lamp although the pictures within them were dark and anonymous and at the fugitive sparkle of reflected light from the several Venetian mirrors on the walls.

'Oh, very romantic,' she was sarcastic. 'All we want now is somebody outside with a mandolin playing "O sole mio"! You needn't have bothered, you know—I've come to talk business.'

'Not romantic at all,' he contradicted. 'For romance, we would need a pink shade on the lamp—it's more flattering to a woman's complexion. You see, I know all the—er—angles.'

'And I could do with some flattering,' she grinned as she indicated her well-worn jeans and the T-shirt which had long ago lost its pristine whiteness. 'But honestly—like I said—you needn't have bothered. I haven't crept down for a necking session.'

'You disappoint me,' and his beaky nose twitched in distaste. 'I'm not only disappointed, I'm repelled by your coarseness. Is it assumed to—er—put me off?'

'Just so you don't get any ideas.' The fire was going merrily by this time and she crossed to it and held out a bare foot to the flames. 'I want a favour, the use of my car to take your mother to Rome and if I promise to be very careful about the driving—I'd only use it for the journey down, I wouldn't try to drive in Rome or anything stupid like that—the traffic is hair raising. . . . I don't even know why I'm bothering to ask your permission. What I ought to do is break down the garage door and *take* the damn thing whether you like it or not! Or,' she threw him a sparkling glance and continued meditatively, 'I could ask your nephew for a lift . . .?'

'Which wouldn't get you to Rome,' Nicolo grinned wolfishly. 'Sandro leaves tomorrow morning for Florence and he'll be there for at least two weeks. . . .'

'You've arranged that deliberately,' she accused with her nose in the air. 'Well, you've wasted your time, let me tell you. I'm well past the age when pretty boys appealed to me—oh lord, what's happening?' She became rueful. 'I was going to ask so nicely and the first thing I know, I'm losing my temper. You definitely bring out the worst in me.'

'Mmm,' he was rueful as well. 'We shall certainly have a stormy beginning to our marriage. . . .'

'And that's another thing,' she interrupted. 'This marriage you're on about—I went along with it because of your mother, that was all. I didn't expect you to take it seriously—face saving—a temporary thing, I wasn't keen on deceiving the signora but it was better than risking her being ill but you've put it all on a permanent basis. . . .'

'Which has the virtue of respectability,' he pointed out lazily, so that she had the idea he was playing a cat and mouse game with her, almost purring while he pinned her down with a velvety paw.

'And you're so hot on respectability,' she sneered, remembering a time when he hadn't been, couldn't have been or Maris wouldn't have humbled herself so.

'Where you are concerned, yes!' The pinning down paw was no longer velvety, she thought she could feel the prick of sharp claws. 'I would like our relationship to be quite legal before we take it a step further and, more than that, I have your well being to consider. Make no mistake about it, *cara*—we *are* going to be married and I don't understand why you're so reluctant. It will be a good marriage and we'll both of us enjoy it.'

'I shall *not* enjoy it,' she was fierce. 'I wouldn't enjoy anything I was dragooned into—against my will. . . .'

'Claudia,' the claws were withdrawn and the purr was back in his voice. 'It won't be against your will, we both know that. Shall I give you a demonstration?'

'No!' She swung round so that her back was towards him, only too aware that her T-shirt, thin from much washing, was clinging to her bra-less breasts and she was a long way from being as cool and composed as she was pretending. With a little moan, she crossed her arms over her chest. 'I only wanted my car,' she muttered. 'A simple "yes" will do.'

She heard his soft chuckle behind her and felt her palms growing damp. Was this how he'd played with Maris? Teasing until it became more than she could bear—teasing softly—about the only weapon which would have pierced her cousin's hard but thin shell of sophistication. Poor Maris, so brittle and worldly. Deliberately, she let her mind go back to that night—to a desperate, white-faced cousin—shocked and stunned but who had recovered enough to be vengeful although half out of her mind with humiliation. The exercise did Claudia good, she swung back to face him.

'Do I get my car?' she demanded peremptorily. 'I told you, that was what I came for. I don't need a demonstration—it wouldn't prove anything, one way or the other. I'm human, like anybody else. Human and a bit weak.' She chanced a look up into his face and the triumphant quality of his smile upset her precarious balance.

'All right, damn you,' she ground it out between her teeth. 'I'll do as you say. We'll be married and much joy you'll get out of it! Within a week, you'll be wishing you never set eyes on me, I promise you that! Now, may I have my car or not?'

'Since you ask so nicely,' he surveyed her flushed face intently, 'and because I find it hard to deny you anything—yes, I will permit you to drive to Rome. . . .'

' "Give me liberty or give me death," ' she quoted savagely. 'You will permit! Ha! When do we go?'

'In three days' time, I think that would be best.' Nicolo considered the angles aloud. 'Tomorrow, Sandro leaves for Firenze—allow my mother another day to prepare for the journey, perhaps two. Ten days should be enough for your shopping although my mother will demand twice as long. See she doesn't overtire herself, *cara*.'

Having got her own way, Claudia was prepared to be generous. 'Of course,' she snorted softly. 'Do you think she could manage a trip out to Bracciano one afternoon? I've always wanted to go there, see the lake and the Castello Orsini. . . .'

'I doubt you'll have time,' his eyes twinkled. 'You see, I know my mother and you don't, so don't be disappointed if she fills your days with shopping. I've a small place in Trevignano, we can go there any time and a week would be better than a flying visit, hmm? You could paint—the village is very picturesque. One thing though, Sandro is going to Firenze but he probably won't stay there for long. He'll be back in Rome as soon as possible. Use him carefully, *cara*—you'll find Mama doesn't encourage him and I advise you to do the same.'

'Afraid he'll run off with your girlfriend?' she jeered and watched as his smile became enigmatic.

'Sandro has hidden depths!'

For the second time, she slid into her nightie and climbed into the high bed. She didn't feel victorious but strangely at peace as though she'd been relieved of a burden. Her way of escape was open, she could take it if she wanted, she was no longer like a piece on a chess board to be pushed about from square to square—she didn't mind being coerced a little but she objected to being compelled and Nicolo was very good at coercion. His dark brown velvety voice had an almost hypnotic quality so that she could nearly believe he was sincere—that it wasn't all a game he was playing for some hidden reason of his own. The touch of his hands had been gentle and his goodnight kiss had been very sweet, but controlled, as though he wanted the spark between them to start only a warming, comforting glow and not a conflagration.

But Maris—she blinked in the bright moonlight which streamed into the room through the drawn curtains—it was strange how she could always think of Maris while James seemed to have retreated into the past, to be no more than a dim, shadowy, half-forgotten figure she could no longer even make out. Perhaps she was jealous of Maris, or perhaps it was all a bit Freudian after all— something deep within her reminding her that the Gabrielli man wasn't to be trusted. That he'd treated Maris badly and what he could do to one woman, he could do just as easily to another.

Not that she'd the slightest intention of marrying him! She'd said she would but that was only a compound of sheer temper and the desire to have the Allegro so that she could escape—he would know that, surely? But he must have the devil's own impudence to imagine that, knowing what she did about him and her cousin, she'd marry him for any reason at all, much less a purely physical one which would soon burn itself out. With a grunt of disgust at the way her mind was rambling round in circles, she closed her eyes, turned her back on the moonlight and went to sleep.

At breakfast, Sandro was full of a whimsical melancholy. 'I may be the head of the family in theory,' he said with a sad merriment, 'but it means little to Zio Nicolo. When I was younger, I rebelled but I soon learned better. It did me no good, you see. My zio is a man who likes to have his own way. You have a saying in English—He who pays the piper, calls the tune—that's right, isn't it?'

'Yes,' Claudia refilled both their coffee cups, feeling rather uncomfortable and wishing that Nicolo hadn't breakfasted earlier and gone out. She eyed his abandoned chair with a smouldering look, the used cup and saucer, the slight scatter of crumbs on the cloth and the knife, showing traces of cherry jam, tossed down carelessly beside the plate. He ought to have known she was in no mood to cope with Sandro and there would be no relief—the signora breakfasted in bed.

'Yes,' she said it again brightly in case he hadn't heard her first mutter. 'That's exactly how we say it although we've another saying—That the devil has the best tunes.'

Sandro agreed with her, 'My zio certainly has some good tunes but not today, I think. You and Nonna Venetia are going to Rome and I had hoped you would allow me to escort you. I could have driven you there myself and, I know it sounds boastful but nobody knows Rome better than I do—I would have planned excursions, enjoyed showing you everything. It would have made your stay there much more enjoyable but my zio insists I go to Firenze, we have vineyards near there and there have been a few problems. . . .' He looked so like a disappointed cherub that Claudia smiled at him consolingly and became positively heartening.

'I'm sure you'll sort it all out in no time at all and we're not going for a few days yet. You never know, you might get your business cleared up more quickly than you think and be back in Rome before your nonna and I are ready to leave. In any

case,' she crinkled her face into a rueful smile, 'I've
seen your car and I can't imagine your nonna
travelling in a sports coupé and being blown
about. I'm sure she'd prefer to travel in something
a little more sedate.' She had been going to quote
another extenuating circumstance—that she
couldn't have ridden in a white sports car but that
could involve an explanation and she didn't want
to talk about it. Sandro's bump of curiosity was
too well developed, he'd want to know too much.
A curt 'I don't like white cars' wouldn't satisfy
him. Instead, she manufactured a kind smile and
spread a hot roll with too much butter so that the
cherry jam slithered off and landed on her plate
with a plop.

'My zio depends on me for these little errands
when he has more pressing affairs in hand,'
Sandro made it mournful. 'But in this case, when
the pressing affair is his marriage, I am only too
willing. A short time ago, I was to have been
married, you know but it all came to nothing. . . .'

'So you said before,' Claudia reminded him
tartly but at the distressed look in his large, dark
eyes, she relented. 'We've another English saying—
There's more fish in the sea than ever came out of
it.'

'Which means. . .? Sandro inched his chair, his
plate and his coffee cup nearer to her and reached
across for another roll, his shoulder hard against
hers as he leaned against her.

'That you've plenty of time,' she temporised.

'But,' his air of melancholy increased, 'when you
see the fish you want being caught by another
man. . . .'

'Pooh!' she became bracing. 'Like I said, there's
plenty more.'

Large, dark eyes surveyed her sadly, almost as if she was to blame for something and there was a mute plea in their depths. 'I cannot afford to fish the same waters as my zio—that is the difference between us, him and me. He has everything while I am very poor. What woman would take me in preference to him when I can offer nothing but my undying love. My zio has it all, the air of command—of course that is because he is so much older than me and Nonna Venetia brought him up to think himself a god among men, whereas my little mother died so very soon after I was born and I think my father hated me for that. . . . He seemed to think if it hadn't been for me, his beloved little wife would have lived. . . .'

'That's nonsense,' Claudia tried to be brisk—she was rapidly becoming tired of all this moaning and mournfulness. 'You only think that, you don't know it and it's quite useless to feel that way about your uncle. He's only a man, the same as you are.'

Sandro nodded, 'But what a man—he has everything—this house, I was so very young, I had to believe him when he said I couldn't afford to keep it but even so—when I sold it to him—he didn't actually pay me for it, you know. He made a, I think you would call it a Trust for me, and I have only the income from it. And there were the vineyards near Firenze, other properties—he said he was saving them for the future Gabriellis—I try not to be bitter about it. . . .'

'Bitterness does no good,' Claudia said it emphatically from a wealth of experience—she would have liked to tell him that bitterness warped, that it turned life into a wilderness of dust and ashes but something stopped her—a feeling that, once started, she might say too much and Sandro wasn't her ideal when it came to a recipient of confidences.

'Besides,' she tried to be kind, 'I much prefer you when you're in a happy mood. . . .'

'With you, I would always be happy.' His reply came promptly and he edged a little nearer to her so that their shoulders were touching. 'Something happened to me when I first saw you. . . .'

'Another few seconds and my nephew will be swearing undying love for you, *cara*,' Nicolo's voice came, deep and sardonic behind them. '*Nipote*, I thought you to be on your way to Firenze.'

Sandro turned to the source of the interruption but Claudia remained as she was, lowering her head to consider the remains of her breakfast with deep absorption—if there was going to be a family squabble, she wanted no part of it.

'I'm going, slave driver!' Sandro made it sound amusing, 'I was just saying goodbye to your *fidanzata*. You see how he treats me, Claudia? Like an errand boy, a *fattorino*—after you two are married, he will probably forbid me the house. My zio has a jealous streak,' he smiled gayly and then, 'All right, I go, I go—don't scowl at me so, Zio Nico; it makes you look old. *Arrivederci*,' and Claudia, still with her eyes on her plate, heard the door slam as he went off. Her *fidanzato* took the vacated chair and pushed a clean cup and saucer towards her.

'If the coffee's still hot, I'll have some,' he didn't sound anything but coolly amused. 'Sandro has been trying to flirt with you?'

'More of a bid for sympathy,' she growled as she poured for him.

'Sandro's technique.' She didn't look but she knew he was smiling. 'And when your heart has melted with pity for him, he looks at you with eyes which are swimming with emotion and you're lost! It works every time.'

'I wasn't melting with pity,' she denied. 'I was trying to cheer him up and there's no chance that I'd ever fall for that hoary old line.'

'You've heard it so often?'

'Some,' she admitted brightly. 'A girl does, you know. It's quite an old routine.'

'So, if you've heard it before, you'll be wise before and not after the event, I hope.' He put a hand on her shoulder and pulled her towards him. 'I would like to be able to trust my wife. Sandro has a lot of appeal and he's often here. . . .'

'You either trust me or you don't!' Claudia heard herself being surly. 'And if you don't, you know what you can do! You can call it off, I shan't complain, I assure you.'

'But that would disappoint Mama,' he pointed out. 'She's looking forward to dressing you. . . .'

'And that's another thing,' she snarled. 'I like your mother, in fact I can't understand how she ever managed to produce a tyrant like you but I won't be pushed around like a puppet. The fact is, I'm not interested in clothes—they bore me to death—I don't care what I wear as long as it's clean and decent. Buy your mama a doll and let her dress that!'

'Now you're being deliberately obstructive.' She was chided.

'And I'll go on being bloody obstructive,' she flared. 'I've a right, haven't I? I came here for some peaceful painting and look at the mess you've landed me in. I've done nothing worthwhile since I arrived, I've just wasted my time and, unlike you, I have my living to earn. . . .'

'You came here with your little head stuffed full of vengeful nonsense.' She watched as his nostrils thinned and then flared with irritation. 'Stupid girl! I thought you'd forgotten about that, or better still, put it out of your mind but no, you're still clinging to it. I told you it was a dangerous game to play, you don't know what you're up against.'

'Oh yes I do,' she almost squealed with rage—how dared he call her a 'stupid girl'! Her eyes hardened in defiance. 'And what's wrong with a little healthy hate and a desire to get even, I'd like to know? Why is it you Gabriellis can go round doing just what you like and get away with it but me, I'm supposed to forgive and forget? A little while ago, about four days, to be precise, I thought I was wrong to feel the way I did, I thought I was letting the past ruin my life and I decided to give it up and forget but every damn word you say brings it back and when you go into your "Lord of Creation" act, you make me boil! You've tricked me, pawed me about—take your hands off me at once—and got me so I don't know whether I'm on my head or my heels. You've even arranged a marriage for me! Who the hell do you think you are, a superior being? I said take your hands off me! You don't own me, not yet!'

'So much bad temper and so early in the morning,' he reproved. 'I'm glad Mama has her breakfast in bed—she wouldn't like to hear you being so noisy or so rude.'

'I don't give a damn.' Claudia tried to twitch her shoulders from his grasp but there was steel in his fingers and she almost cried aloud with the pain of his grasp where those fingers pressed on the thin layer of flesh which covered her bones. If he pressed any harder, she had the idea that something would snap and since there was no cessation of the pressure, she went still and quiet.

'Listen to me, you foolish woman,' he growled it softly. 'Perhaps I'd better remind you, I saved your life once, you owe me something for that. No,' as she opened her mouth to blast him to Kingdom Come, 'don't talk, just listen. There will be no more thoughts of revenge, do you hear me?' He emphasised each word with a shake which set the teeth rattling in her head. 'The past is dead and buried. . . .'

'So's my gratitude to you for saving my life,' she interrupted. 'You can't have it both ways. I must remember that you rescued me but I'm to forget why you had to. Make up your mind, please. Do I remember or do I forget?' Every inch of her registered defiance and her mouth had a mutinous curve.

'Forget everything but this.' His mouth swooped on hers while his hands pulled her closer so that she could feel the thrust and the hard demand of his body against hers. The kiss wasn't a kind one, his mouth was as painful as his hands, but somehow it killed off her temper and reduced her defiance to a mute surrender so that she slumped against him and her eyes drifted shut while his lips took their toll of her mouth, her cheeks, the curve of her throat and when he at last released her, there were tears of humiliation sliding down from under her closed lids. Humiliation at her own weakness and disgust for the treachery of her body, but she was still not beaten.

'F-finished?' she demanded hoarsely. 'What I

mean is, I can take a hint, you don't have to drum it in with a sledge hammer. All right, I admit, we've got something but damn you for taking advantage of it every time you want to get your own way. Now, see what you've done, you've made me cry, you bastard.'

'Pre-wedding nerves,' he diagnosed calmly. 'And as you say—as I've already told you, we have something between us. . . .'

'I wish it was the Atlantic,' Claudia was beginning to recover. 'Or better still, the Pacific, that's bigger. . . .'

'*Cara,*' his mouth hovered over hers threateningly, seducing. 'Stop wagging that sharp little tongue at me or I will silence you in the only way I can. I wish we were already married—I would take you to bed and there would be an end to all this argument and fighting.'

'Don't let a little thing like not being married stop you,' she spat. 'I'm sure it hasn't in the past and why make an exception of me? And don't bother with the niceties, like me being a guest in your house. You can always wriggle out of it by telling yourself I was an unwilling guest. You've a precedent, haven't you— something to do with the Sabine women— I'm not much good at history but I remember that. Go on,' she jeered. 'There's nothing to stop you, only a houseful of doting retainers who will probably look the other way or think you're doing me a tremendous favour. I bet if I screamed my head off they'd all be convinced I was yelling with joy!'

His mouth curved into a delighted smile and his slanting eyes glowed warmly down at her. 'Almost, you tempt me, Claudia, but we have to consider Mama, she's very straitlaced. She wouldn't like it.'

'Neither should I!'

'Liar!' His hand tightened its grasp on her hip and for a moment he held her firmly before putting her back in her chair. 'Now, shall we be serious? In about an hour, Sandro should be ready to leave. I want no mournful parting between you and him and when he looks at you as though you're the only woman in the world, you will ignore it. You are to give him no encouragement at all, you understand? When you next meet him, we will, I hope, be safely married—it won't stop him from trying to make love to you but at least, I shall be in a position to—er—head him off. You will be his aunt and you will treat him as a nephew, a young nephew and I shall be watching so you'd better be careful.'

'Any more orders, sir?' she enquired pertly and then with an aggravated sigh. 'Call it off, do! Let's go away together for a dirty weekend, get it out of our systems—I'm willing if you are. You can always tell your mother you made a mistake, that I'm not, after all, the sort of woman you ought to marry, you could even tell her I'm promiscuous, I won't mind.'

'But I should,' he was grave, 'and Mama would be heartbroken!'

'That one is a Don Giovanni,' the signora observed crisply as Sandro and his white coupé disappeared down the drive in a cloud of dust. 'You know what I mean, Claudia?'

'Self-explanatory,' Claudia giggled. 'In English, we'd call him a flirt or a Don Juan. Your son said Sandro has hidden depths but I haven't discovered any so far.'

'Nicolo is right,' a faint distaste flickered across

the signora's face, gone so quickly that Claudia thought she might have imagined it. 'Too deep and very well hidden—a deceptive young man.' The signora abandoned the subject of Sandro for one nearer her heart. 'This morning, you shall do my portrait—what fee will you pay me?'

'Three pounds,' Claudia was prompt.

'Make it five and call me Mama. I always wanted a daughter, they're so much more fun. Of course, it's nice to have a son but a mother can do so little with a man. Girls can be dressed, they will talk about fashions, coiffeurs, furnishings. . . .'

'Woman talk,' Claudia grinned understandingly. 'Just wait while I get paper and my pastels and you can tell me about how you were dressed when you were young while I'm sketching you.'

'Pastels!' the signora was disappointed. 'You aren't going to do me in oils?'

'Can't afford it,' Claudia choked on a giggle. 'That *would* be five pounds and it would take far too long. Besides, portraits aren't my strong point, at least, not in oils. I'm better at landscapes.' At which, she sped off to collect her materials.

'Here, I think,' the signora said when Claudia returned. 'The light is good, no? And I shall have something to look at.' So Claudia seated herself in front and a little to one side while Nicolo's mama gazed out over the gardens from where she sat, straight-backed on her chair.

All the time Claudia worked, the lady kept up a flow of talk. She didn't chatter—it was only a smooth, one-sided conversation and Claudia, busy, paid very little attention as her sketch grew under her fingers. Some phrases came through.

'And the wedding dress—of course white is out of the question but I think cream would be acceptable—cream satin, slightly stiffened for the skirt which should be quite full. There's nothing better to emphasise a slender waist than a full, slightly stiff skirt. No *décolleté*, I think—a modern trend, I know but I deplore it—for a civil wedding, perhaps, that is not so important, but in a church.'. . .'

Swiftly, the sketch grew—it wasn't so difficult—Nicolo and his mother had the same bone structure and she'd drawn Nicolo thousands of times. His mother was old, the roundness of youth had vanished from her face but the fine skin hadn't creased—it had tightened across the bones with hardly a wrinkle to mar its perfection. The nose wasn't as bold but it was the same nose, thin and beaky.

'You must have looked like Nefertiti when you were young,' she said, apropos of nothing and was rewarded by a delighted chuckle.

'I did, or so everybody told me—I remember going to a fancy dress ball dressed in a Nefertiti costume when I was eighteen and I'm always glad that Nicolo resembles me—a Venetian through and through and not only in looks either. He has brains and ability, that one, and an appreciation of beauty as well as great business sense. Roses for your bouquet, gold ones or perhaps an apricot shade would be better, it's good you have protected your complexion—so many English people come to Italy and bare themselves until they look like walnuts. May I see what you've done?'

'No, you may not.' Claudia was cheerfully blunt as she blended the pastels with gentle strokes of her finger. 'Not until I've finished and then, not if I'm dissatisfied.'

'In your small way, you are as great a tyrant as I am.' But Signora Gabrielli didn't sound displeased. 'Very well, I shall continue to discuss our stay in Rome. I know a good dressmaker—expensive, of course but very quick and reliable—I think we should choose patterns for the bulk of your outfit and pick out the materials to have them made up for you—that way we shall get exactly what we want and a better fit than if they were bought from a shop—and there is another woman, I always go to her for my underwear, she makes the most beautiful stuff, silk and real hand-made lace—a dozen of everything do you think?'

Claudia had run into trouble about the signora's left eye and merely grunted that she couldn't see the need for so much, while she rectified her mistake. 'I'm used to a quiet life,' she explained, 'and I spend most of my time dressed as you see me now,' a wave of her hand indicated her jeans, T-shirt and smock. 'I wouldn't need a quarter of what you're planning.' But then, remembering that shopping was going to be her excuse for getting out on her own, calling on Maris' *avvocat*, going to her cousin's apartment, she softened it a bit. 'But it would be nice to have several changes of clothes, a bit of variety in the evenings—and silk undies—I don't think I've ever had anything as sumptuous as that, certainly not ones trimmed with hand-made lace. They sound quite sybaritic.'

CHAPTER EIGHT

'THIS is an unexpected pleasure, Signora Currey.' Signor Marinotta, Maris' man of affairs, her *avvocato*, beamed with pleasure. Behind the pleasure there was a gleam of relief and Claudia was quick to notice it. 'I took the liberty of writing to you several weeks ago but there was no reply and, since I felt that matters might worsen, I attempted to procure your telephone number but that proved impossible. It is very difficult, signora,' there was a mild reproof in his tones and his old eyes glittered behind his spectacles, 'to represent a client when that client remains incommunicado.'

'Please forgive me, Signor Marinotta.' Since his English was old-fashioned and formal, Claudia tried to match it—besides, she wanted, needed, his co-operation and making him even slightly angry wouldn't get it. 'After my stay in the London clinic, I decided to take a holiday. I've been staying at the Villa Cristal but since I intended travelling about, I didn't leave a forwarding address. Have I done something wrong, signor?'

'Not at all.' Her quiet formality had paid dividends, the old lawyer was now quite kind, almost fatherly. 'On the contrary, signora, it is you who have been wronged.' He retreated behind his desk and became fussy about the disposition of his many papers. 'Your apartment was broken into again, nearly a month ago—understandable when one considers how long it has been empty. Indeed,

132

only to be expected when one remembers it isn't the first time it has happened. But that first time was over a year ago and you were in hospital here, in Rome so, if you recall, I sought your permission to change the locks and when that was done, I gave you a new set of keys. This time, I had to act without direction or consultation with you and had you gone there without seeing me first, you would have found it impossible to enter; your keys wouldn't have fitted.'

'Any damage?' Claudia crossed her ankles and tried to look competent and businesslike.

'Fortunately, no—a mere displacement of articles, nothing was damaged or broken.' He looked pleased as though he was personally responsible for so slight a case of burglary. 'You would not know, signora, but the man who bought the boutique and the floor above it, has turned the workrooms into living accommodation. As soon as he heard movements above his head—where there should have been no movement at all—he phoned the police. Of course, they did not catch the intruder who must have been forewarned by the noise of their coming. But only you have a list of the contents of the apartment so, while I can say truthfully that there was no damage, apart from more broken locks, I cannot say there was no theft.' He tut-tutted and adjusted his spectacles. 'Perhaps, now, you realise the importance of my being able to find you at all times, signora.'

'I do,' Claudia nodded solemnly. 'And I suppose you'd like me to inspect the place. I mean to anyway, signor, so I'll go there at once. May I please have the new set of keys?' And as she stuffed them in her shoulderbag she debated for and against, finally settling on 'for'. 'Later in the week, signor, I believe I shall have a little time to spare and I shall go to the apartment, perhaps stay the night and clear out all my cousin's personal things. The clothes can be sold or given away—her jewellery, I shall send to you—that can be sold,' she gave him a quiet smile of confidence, 'and when I've finished there, I'll send you the keys. As you've pointed out, it's unwise to leave an apartment vacant for too long—an open invitation to thieves—so I'd be glad if you would sell it for me, I shan't be needing it again.'

'As you wish, signora.' His old face expressed no surprise and she guessed he'd read the announcement in the papers—what would the wife of a rich man, with a villa in Tuscany, a house in Trevignano and the lord only knew how many other places, want with an apartment right alongside the noisy Corso? 'And the money, signora; when the apartment, the furnishings and the jewellery is sold?'

'Put it in the bank with the rest.' She was curt, realised it and smiled to soften the curtness.

'But so much money,' he protested. 'The sale of the boutique and workrooms realised a large sum which I know you've never touched. It should all be invested to bring you a steady income. Leaving it on deposit in the bank is wasteful when it could be earning more money for you but I suppose you will discuss this matter with Signor Gabrielli and let him decide where and when you invest. You couldn't have a better adviser, the signor is greatly esteemed for his business acumen.'

'Mmm, I hadn't thought of that but I suppose you're right.' Claudia rose and politely made her escape before she said something she shouldn't. She hadn't the slightest intention of doing any such thing but her agreement did serve to end the interview. In truth, she didn't know what to do with the money, the only thing she did know was that she couldn't spend it, not a penny of it. She never had and she never would! Perhaps, one day she'd find a charity—a really deserving one—and give the whole lot away. A rueful smile curled her lips at the thought. Maris wouldn't have approved of that, she'd never been particularly charity minded!

The *avvocato*'s chambers were very close to the Palazzo di Giustizia—did Italian lawyers have chambers, she wondered? And while she waited to hail the first passing taxi, she pictured the little man in a black robe, bands and a white wig, hurrying between courtrooms. The image conjured up was so funny she laughed aloud and she was still chuckling when a taxi drew up to her signal.

With her inside, it crossed the river by the Ponte Margherita, went round the Piazza del Popolo and headed straight down the Corso to turn left into a seeming maze of small streets and finally drew up outside what had been Maris' boutique. Claudia got out, paid the driver and looked hard at the shop window. The man who had bought it, whoever he was—wasn't in Maris' class either for design or for window dressing but that was all behind her now and she slipped in through the side entrance and up the four flights of stairs unnoticed.

There were a few scars on the door where the locks had been changed, ugly deep scratches which spoiled the glossy appearance but other than that, it looked exactly as it had been when she'd been here last. Inside the door, nothing had changed— as though it had all been wrapped up in plastic to preserve it. The rooms still contained Maris' white, cubic, leather-upholstered furniture and the tables with their black glass tops—it was all very neat and tidy—Signor Marinotta had arranged for a cleaner to come once a week so it didn't smell stale or as if it hadn't been used for two years, and with a swift glance around the *salotto,* she dropped her bag on one of the tables and went into the main bedroom. The only truly personal room in the apartment—it breathed of Maris as though she still lingered there.

It was here, in the bedroom, that the intruder seemed to have concentrated. The two tiers of drawers containing underwear and woollens, concealed by the sliding doors of the wardrobe which ran the length of the wall, had been tossed over by searching hands, their contents were tumbled and untidy and the hanging clothes had been searched as well. Now, separates and suits were mixed in among day and evening dresses— Maris had always been orderly and methodical when it came to clothes. Claudia left the doors open and retreated to the bed, where she sat down and looked at the rest of the room.

It was, like the rest of the apartment, a symphony in black and white. White, deep-piled carpet; glossy black skin bedside rugs; white filmy drapes from the canopy over the huge bed; black silk sheets and pillow cases—everything to enhance and nothing to detract from her cousin's copper-haired, white-skinned beauty. But Claudia thought it was an uncomfortable room and not one she'd ever wish to inhabit, it wasn't restful.

With a sigh, she crossed to the dressing table— also white—a flat top on curved legs and supporting a set of three oval mirrors. As she moved, she caught sight of herself reflected in several of the mirrors which seemed almost to line the walls—Maris must have had narcissistic tendencies, all these mirrors. There were two obvious drawers in the dressing table, one on either side—shallow little things which held hankies and other small articles—and a central drawer which wasn't so obvious. It had no handle and its edges were concealed by some gilt moulding, but Maris had once told her the trick of it. She slid her hand underneath the top, pressed up on what felt like a springy splinter of wood and heard a satisfying click.

The drawer slid open smoothly and Claudia reached inside to take out the large, flattish silver box in which her cousin had kept her jewellery, to open it and gaze at the contents with surprise. It was all there, as far as she could tell. A string of pearls, very white, hard, smooth and cold—obviously genuine—the emerald-set clasp glittered in the light from the window, flashing green fire. There were at least a dozen gold chains, thick and heavy, not trumpery and all different types and lengths; belchers; ropes; flat, snakey things; some earrings, not many—plain hoops and studs for day wear and big, glittery chandelier ones for evenings. A few brooches to wear on suits; large, semi-precious stones set chunkily in gold and silver and lastly, in its own box, a modern, gold copy of an old Venetian brooch—two cherubs supporting a coronet over a shield set with small pearls and with three larger pearls hanging from it on tiny gold chains—Signora Gabrielli would have loved it.

Besides the silver box, there was another; an old cigar box, but there was nothing of value in it.

Some rings, brooches and earrings, mostly dress jewellery—Claudia called it junk—big, blatant things, some of them broken or damaged. She pushed the silver box into her shoulder bag—it had better not be left here—but the implications of what she'd found were obvious. Anybody with a little professional experience would have found that drawer and would have broken it open if he hadn't known or couldn't find the spring. He wouldn't have bothered tumbling over clothing in search of valuables. It had probably been a young sneak thief looking for some quick and easy plunder—something which could be sold easily and quickly.

Although the *salotto* looked undisturbed, the kitchen had suffered, which seemed to confirm her suspicions about the type of thief. Despite the efforts of the cleaning woman, the kitchen cupboards and the small larder were in a pickle, bearing little resemblance to Maris' love of order and neatness. Cans and jars were muddled in all anyhow but Claudia wasn't domestically minded herself—her only order was in her paint box so she shrugged and walked back to the bedroom, where she sat on the bed and considered the wardrobe.

Here were all the clothes she could want—and they would all fit—she and Maris had been the same size. It would save money to take some of them but she couldn't touch them—nothing to do with hygiene—each garment was in a see-through bag with a cleaner's ticket attached but these things had been Maris' and Maris was dead—end off story! Perhaps, if she was desperate, but even then it would have to be something new, something her cousin had never worn.

Claudia didn't bother with a taxi back to the

hotel, it wasn't far to the Spanish Steps so she walked, pausing at a corner of a street bar for a cup of coffee and drinking it while she thought up a good excuse for wasting a whole morning. Nico's Mama would consider it a waste if she didn't come back loaded down and staggering under the weight of boxes and packages—all of which had to contain clothing. No trousseau was complete until it had six of everything, preferably a dozen!

Signora Gabrielli had lunched in the rooftop restaurant and Claudia found her in the sitting room of their suite, fanning herself lethargically. Claudia noticed the lack of colour, the faint film of perspiration and the faint bruising under the signora's eyes—Nico's mother looked drained and somehow vulnerable, quite unlike her usual, ebullient self and this wasn't an act, of that she was certain.

The signora was a superb actress so that over the weeks, Claudia had begun to doubt Nico's story of a heart condition—a ploy, a sob story he'd told to get his own way—that was what she had thought, almost made herself believe because it was more convenient to think that way— it took the onus off her but now, seeing what effect a little activity had produced, she came to the reluctant conclusion that Nico had every reason to be worried—she was worried herself.

'You should be lying down,' she scolded.

'I was waiting for you to return, I thought you might have bought something,' the signora rallied and sounded almost like her usual self. 'You've wasted a whole morning!'

'Not wasted—a holiday from shopping.' Claudia didn't want to mention Maris or the *avvocato*, certainly not the apartment, so she soothed.

'There's nothing like taking a break when things are getting on top of you. I felt I was being buried under a pile of clothes.'

'Merely the basis of a wardrobe,' the signora brushed aside her complaints as she rose to her feet—but very slowly. 'Very little really—you'll find you need to add to it from time to time.'

Claudia abandoned the subject and tried a new one. 'Have you heard from Nico?' She had been going to say 'him' but thought better of it. To the signora, Nico was perfection personified and she wouldn't understand anybody being less besotted than herself.

'A telephone call soon after you left.' Their progress towards the bedroom was slow, Nico's mother stopped frequently to admire the view from the windows or to comment on a flower arrangement—all done to cover up her breathlessness, Claudia was convinced, but at the mention of her son's name, the lady became more alive. 'Men have no idea of the importance of other things—always they consider first what is important to them. Nico proposes to visit us on Thursday, which is the day for the final fitting of the wedding dress so I have had to rearrange the schedule. I've put back the fitting until Friday, which is just as well since Nico will be able to bring me one or two things which are necessary and he may now take us instead to Fragiacomo's for shoes. If you don't like what you find there, we can try Maud Frizon but her prices are ruinous.'

So, Nico was coming on Thursday—today was Monday—which meant that she had two days of grace. After slipping the older woman into a négligé and seeing her resting quietly on the bed with the air conditioning going full pelt, Claudia went back to her own bedroom to sort herself out. Two days of grace, that was a laugh for a start. Already, she was more than half committed to this crazy marriage—money spent on clothes—a wedding dress nearly finished—it was laughable to think of running out at this late stage. She wouldn't be thinking of it, only the alternative seemed worse.

Claudia kicked off her shoes and, still fully clothed, sprawled on the bed, face down on a mound of pillows. Work it out calmly, she told herself, but even thinking about the alternative ruined her rest. She turned over on to her back and contemplated the ceiling.

Nico didn't love her, he hadn't said so—that was one pill she'd have to swallow and after that, she'd have to stomach his affair with Maris. Could she take a marriage like that? Revelation came and she rolled back on to her stomach to press her hot face back into the pillows—yes, she could! He'd been in love with Maris—no matter for how short a time—he'd been Maris' lover. He'd also done the dirty on her, turning her away when he'd grown tired of the affair—when Maris had been expecting marriage. His rejection had been a contributory factor in the deaths of James and Maris. It was hard to believe that under his surface charm, beneath his layer of generous good humour and understanding he could be so cold hearted, so implacable, but she had proof of it.

And that proof didn't make a damn bit of difference to the way she felt. Saint or sinner or just plain man, she loved him and it didn't matter two hoots what he'd done or what he might do in the future. She, Claudia, had balked at the thought of wearing Maris' clothes but she wasn't above taking her cousin's man—which was a laugh in itself although she felt more like crying about it. And there was his mother—bossy but kind and very lovable and as delicate as an old, pressed flower between the pages of a book—brittle so that one clumsy touch would make her crumble into pieces. Maybe Nico could live with a thing like that on his conscience but Claudia didn't think she could. Anyway, she had two more days to think about it—no need to make decisions yet.

But Tuesday and Wednesday weren't too bad, all things considered. Nico's mother decided to shop in the evenings, braving the tired irritability of shop assistants who had been on their feet since nine in the morning, rather than face the heat, the blinding sunlight and the stuffiness of taxis which the signora insisted all smelled as though they'd been carting refuse instead of passengers, and Claudia was forced to watch as commitment piled on commitment with every new dress bag and box of underwear which mounted up in the bottom of her wardrobe.

Nico arrived early on Thursday morning and Claudia, very much against her will, felt sorry for him. Driving from the villa to Rome was no joke as she had cause to know. It was a journey of nearly two hundred miles, and to arrive this early he must have started out around dawn, but her pity didn't make her spare him. His mother was still in bed, having eaten nothing at breakfast and he'd hardly had time to pour the coffee he'd ordered before Claudia started to make her point.

'All this is too much for your mother,' she snapped. 'It's almost too much for me! The best thing you can do is to take her back to the villa when you return this evening.'

'You also, I think.' He eyed her pale face with

the faint smudges of fatigue around her eyes and the weary droop of her shoulders. 'I was expecting something like this, Mama always throws herself into things, overdoes it. . . .'

'And she's not a young woman.' Claudia couldn't control her irritability, brought on by sheer weariness and worry so that she sounded tart. 'Have you any idea of the mound of stuff she thinks necessary? I shall never wear half of it! I know she's being kind and of course, I'm grateful but it's all so needless and she's going to make herself ill. Today, for instance, she says we're going out to buy shoes and since you're here to take us, it will either be in the morning or afternoon—just when it's hottest and it isn't as though I need shoes, not the number of pairs she thinks I should have. It'll all take hours and then your mother will be too tired to eat properly at dinner time.' Her eyes sparkled very green and she whirled on him fiercely. 'Do something about it, can't you?'

'Certainly.' His lashes drooped over his oblique eyes and somehow he managed to look both innocent and conspiratorial at one and the same time. 'We will leave Mama here to rest and I shall take you to buy your shoes. When that is done, we will have a meal before I drive you both back to the villa. Will that do?'

'No, it won't.' She was unreasonably triumphant although she tried hard not to let it show. 'Because you decided to come today, without consulting your mother to see if it was convenient or not, she's had to delay the last fitting of the wedding dress until tomorrow, so I can't leave yet.' Fate was seemingly on her side for once—if he would remove his mother and himself together with all the luggage and leave her here alone, she would have time to think without any pressures. Without being concious of it, she became reasonable, persuasively reasonable.

'If you'd take your mother and all the things we've bought,' she continued, 'it would leave me very little to carry. Oh dear,' she gave a gulp of distress, 'I must be more tired than I thought, I was thinking in terms of trains and letting you know where and when to meet me, I'd completely forgotten my car. . . .'

'After making such a fuss about having it?' He was mocking her and she flushed. 'The woman who was going to break down a door to get it—who pleaded for it!'

'I'm tired too,' she almost snarled. 'I can't remember everything—more than a week of it sitting in the garage here while we coped with taxis, always phoning for transport—you get so you depend on public transport—but I was right about having it, it'll make everything easier. I can drive up and you can expect me some time on Saturday evening. How's that?'

'Very convenient,' he purred it and she glanced at him suspiciously, but he was still looking innocent. 'And the wedding dress? If you need a final fitting, I presume it's not yet finished?'

'N-no, but it shouldn't take much longer and it could be posted on if it isn't ready by Saturday,' she smiled artlessly to cover the sick, shuddering feeling in her stomach—two alternatives and she was making space for them—angling for the chance to escape when she knew in her heart she wasn't going to take that chance but it *had* to be there otherwise, how could she walk away from it—turn her back on it and choose instead an unknown future. Just two days, she prayed silently. Two days, that was all! Quiet days when she could think and prepare herself, maybe even think up a new excuse for what she intended to do.

'I think that's a very good plan of mine,' she forced conviction into her voice, as much to convince herself as him. 'Rome's not the place to be at this time of the year and I shan't stay a moment longer than's absolutely necessary; it's like living in a furnace. Your Mama may protest a bit but she won't mean it, not really. She'll be only too glad to get back to the villa and have a bit of peace.'

'Why do I get the idea I'm marrying a managing woman?' he murmured.

'Possibly because you are!' she smiled frankly. 'I've been looking after my own affairs for the last six or seven years, ever since my mother died. I'm twenty-five, not a girl any longer and I suppose I've got into the habit of arranging things for myself. Probably just as well,' she made a little grimace. 'It toughened me up and after the accident, when I was quite alone. . . .' A thought struck her, 'Your mother doesn't seem to know anything about that. . . .'

'Nobody does, I hope.' But he wasn't as indifferent as he sounded, she was sure of it. 'Didn't you notice I deliberately left your maiden name out of the announcement?'

'Why? Oh, I see, you were ashamed of Maris, perhaps?'

'Nothing of the sort,' he snorted gently and pushed his cup across to her for a refill. 'I was being my usual kind, considerate self—attempting to save you any little pain. If I'd put Claudia Currey née Venables it might have connected you with your cousin and the whole sorry story of the accident would have been splashed over the papers again. I didn't think you'd want that.'

'Very considerate,' and she made one last attempt to make him see sense, consoling herself by deciding that if he didn't, wouldn't, then he had nobody to blame but himself. 'I'd rather not marry you, if you don't mind, I can't see how it's going to work or how we could possibly suit each other. Oh, I know,' she waved him to silence, 'there's this thing we have but it only operates at close quarters, doesn't it? And it's really nothing but good, old-fashioned sex. It'll soon burn itself out, I'm sure—feed on itself until there's nothing left. One morning, we'll both wake up, happier and wiser people and on that morning, it would be a pity if we were in bed together.'

'*Cara.*' Despite her protest and half-hearted wriggling, he pulled her out of her chair to sit on his knee. 'There's an old proverb saying that sleep begets wisdom—I believe in it firmly so, I shall be wise every morning when I wake and I shall be very happy to find you beside me. We won't talk about this any more, the wheels have been set in motion. . . .'

'And I'm to be minced!—in cream satin with a full, slightly stiffened skirt, no décollétage because your Mama doesn't think it would be proper and a bouquet of apricot roses! Oh well,' she slumped against his broad chest and heaved a sigh of resignation. 'Don't say I didn't warn you—whatever happens in the future—it's your fault!'

'Precisely!' He tipped up her chin with a long finger and her eyes closed just before their lips met. In the middle of a very pleasant drowning sensation, she discovered that she liked his obstinacy and single-mindedness and that it would be absolute heaven to let this thing go forward to its inevitable conclusion. James wouldn't haunt her and maybe, after a while, she'd be able to forget the look on Maris' face when he had rejected her—or would she have to live in terror forever that, one day, he'd show her that face, cold and disdainful as he told her they were finished?

Gently, she pushed herself away from him and slithered off his knee, feeling very cold and alone but she talked to cover it. 'Very experienced!' she made it almost an accusation and blinked at his reply.

'No more so than any other man.' He shrugged and his air of mockery grew deeper. 'I specialised in footloose ladies with no desire for domesticity. Hearts were never involved or broken, I hope.'

Oh, but they had been—at least one! The memory made her acid. 'Enough play for one morning—I have to go shopping for shoes and I'd have a quieter mind if you'd persuade your mother to spend the morning in bed and better still, go back to the villa with you this evening—she's not only making herself ill, she's making me feel like a deserving charity.'

'She's generous and she likes you,' his mouth curved into a smile. 'Get yourself ready for a shopping spree, *cara*, while I have a word with Mama.'

'I am ready,' and at the shake of his head, 'I am!'

'Not to come shopping with me! Be sensible, Claudia,' he eyed her jeans and T-shirt with obvious disfavour and gestured at his own pale fawn, thin slacks, his brown silk shirt, his pigskin casuals and his fawn jacket. 'You'll make me look overdressed.'

'Well, you didn't have to tart yourself up to see me,' she muttered, but she went off to her bedroom without any further fuss although, as she dressed herself in one of her new Italian skirts and topped it with a mix-and-match shirt, stuffing her feet into her one and only pair of city-type shoes, she had to admit it was nice to be decently dressed for a change—even she was beginning to tire of her too-casual casuals.

Brushing her short, silvery hair into a halo about her face and standing back from the mirror, she decided she didn't look too bad. The skirt was plain white linen, cut with a swing to it and the shirt was in dusty shades of pink, blue and khaki. But it would be a pity to deck herself out in new clothes and leave her face naked, so she did that as well and finished off with a smear of pink lipstick before she crowned her efforts with her deplorable straw hat.

'I know! It looks awful,' she excused herself when she returned to the lounge and found him waiting patiently. 'But it's the only hat I have and I must wear it. I'll take it off when we go into the shops. Did you . . .?'

'Mama says I'm a bully but we've managed to reach a compromise.' His eyes slid over her with an appreciative glint in their darkness. 'She refused, of course; she always does, but she'll go back with me if only to spare you worry. But she insists on being present at the fitting, so we go back tomorrow—in the evening when it's cooler. We could all go together, you'll have finished your shopping by then, surely?'

Damn him! As soon as he put in an appearance, he started to take over. 'My car,' she reminded him sternly.

'You could drive behind me. . . .'

'And slow you up, not likely! The Allegro's getting on and I don't like to push it. I won't leave it behind, besides,' she closed her mouth and gave him what she hoped was a mysterious look, 'I've a little private business of my own that needs attention.'

They walked out through the foyer, between the square marble columns and into the bright sunshine. It wasn't too hot yet and Claudia took advantage of it.

'Shall we walk? It's quite pleasant now and it's not far.'

'If you wish.' Nico sounded indulgent and they descended the Spanish Steps side by side. 'It's better in the Spring,' he told her. 'They have azaleas all along the terraces. You didn't see much of Rome when you were here before, did you?'

'Sightseeing's difficult when one's encased in plaster and confined to a hospital bed,' she pointed out tartly. 'And when one's face looks as though it's been run over by a tram.'

'Then,' he was judicious, 'after we've bought the shoes, would you like to see the Pantheon? It's one of the best preserved of the ancient monuments.'

'Couldn't we go there first?'

'No,' but his smile was encouraging. 'We'll get the shopping done, have lunch and save the Pantheon for the afternoon. Mama's given me a list of what you need and we're not to forget cream satin slippers.'

They strolled on down the steps, Claudia interested and peeping at the work of the many artists.

'Just think,' she chuckled, 'if it hadn't been for your high-handed ways, I might have been one of these,' she waved around at the motley crew. 'A bit scruffy but quite at home and I bet I'd have shown a profit on a day's work!'

CHAPTER NINE

Shopping with Nico was more fun than with his mother and the service was better— damsels flocked to attend to his needs and if Claudia had been shocked at the way the signora spent money, Nico's performance robbed her of speech. He didn't empty his purse, he tipped up the whole Italian mint and let the lira flow regardless. Of course, as she told herself frequently, he hadn't really spent so much, it just sounded a terrifying amount in lira. Translated into sterling, it ceased to frighten her but she certainly acquired a lot of shoes.

'I'm filling Mama's list,' he was grave. 'If we go back to the hotel with anything less, she'll insist on doing it all again tomorrow. Now for lunch.'

Claudia looked at the Pantheon with an artist's eye and found it complete and satisfying. The squareish Greek-style porch with its gigantic monolithic columns fitted on to the circular body of the building—a complete whole and not out of place at all. She passed through the bronze doors, sliding her fingers gently across the surfaces and stood in the circle of light made by the sunlight streaming through the open roundel in the great dome. It was an artist's dream of light and shadow, style and proportion. Her guide book said that Hadrian had built this; a modest man who gave the credit to the builder of the original Pantheon which had been destroyed by fire. It had stood here for nearly two thousand years—which put her petty little affairs in the correct perspective.

'The dome is bigger than your St Paul's,' Nico teased her from behind in a low murmur. 'Has it been worth the visit?'

'I'd like to have seen it when it was new,' she sighed. 'When the statues were in place. . . .'

'Then console yourself with something which should appeal to the artist in you, come and worship at Raphael's tomb.'

But once back in the hotel, all the peace and serenity deserted her so that when, on Friday morning, Nico took them to the dressmaker, Claudia was a bundle of nerves. She'd at last made up her mind—she would stay, not run away and she would marry him. Perhaps what they had would be enough—she would make it enough, nobody could expect roses all the way! She covered her mood of resignation with an appearance of enthusiasm, for the signora's sake, and resisted the impulse to put out her tongue at Nico when his mother banished him from the proceedings.

She followed his mother up the stairs, reminding herself of Mary's Little Lamb—being led to the slaughter! And once inside the fitting room, she managed to put herself into a frame of mind where she was nothing more than a dressmaker's dummy, albeit one which could move as directed. She allowed herself to be nearly stripped and inserted into a long, flounced slip, although she made a face at the number of flounces and ruffles.

'It will help to hold the skirt out,' the signora caught her involuntary grimace of distress, 'otherwise the weight of the demi-train will pull it against you when you walk.'

Claudia, self-disciplined to a mute acceptance, merely nodded. She hadn't even known there was to be a train, demi or otherwise, but she didn't speak in case her tongue refused to utter the conventional platitudes and insisted on saying what she really thought—which was that she wished she was dead! The mere, silent acknowledgment to herself that she loved Nico—and not only physically—seemed to have opened the floodgates of emotion, but emotion had no place here—this was the practicality of marriage, the outward show and not for her benefit. So, she stood like a mannequin while the gown was flung over her head, the folds twitched into place and the long row of satin-covered, tiny buttons fastened. There was a slight interval while a stubborn wrinkle in the bodice was removed and then, the signora produced her *pièce de resistance*, a huge veil of fine silk edged with hand-made lace—not new but creamy with age and a perfect match for the gown.

'My grandmother's.' Nico's mother was proud. 'Very carefully saved. My mother wore it and so did I and we are much of a height so it will be the right length. Nico is a taller man than his father and even with high heels and the veil worn over a coronet, you will still be shorter than he is. The flowers?' This last was to the dressmaker who produced a long spray of silk roses like a conjuror bringing a rabbit out of a hat and while her assistant climbed on to a stool to adjust a make-do coronet on Claudia's head and drape the veil over it, the signora thrust the flowers into Claudia's hands and told her to walk.

'Of course, you won't be carrying those.' His mother now had command of the situation and the dressmaker and assistant sank into the background. 'Not such long steps, please and remember, the flowers will be real roses and slightly heavier. Excellent!' and she and the dressmaker beamed at each other while, behind the corner of the veil which concealed her face, Claudia fought hard not to allow tears to stream down her cheeks.

'You don't look very happy.' She and Nicolo were sitting in the rooftop restaurant of the hotel, sipping granitas while his mother was recuperating from the strains of the morning by lying on her bed in her room with a supplementary electric fan blowing cool air over her.

'I'm not,' Claudia made a rueful face. 'Did you know, I stride like a man? It comes of wearing those "deplorable trousers", or so your mother says.' She tried, without a great deal of success, to make a joke of it while she kept one eye on her watch. Only a few hours to get through and she could manage that, surely? Then he and his mother would be on the way back to Tuscany and she could be alone. And that would be a mixed blessing. It would give her time to think, to get herself calm, but the evening and the night loomed ahead, not very invitingly. She'd be alone, but loneliness had never bothered her before so why should the thought of it upset her now?

'And I carry my bouquet all wrong,' she gabbled, 'so I have to practise when I get to the villa. I'm not to look as though I'm cuddling a baby or trying to conceal one.' She thought she'd made a good point there, she'd said that bit about returning to the villa without thinking, she was accepting it at last as a foregone conclusion.

Dark, oblique eyes slanted a smile at her, 'And under all the *presa in giro*, the mockery, the making fun of it, there's a woman who is afraid of being married!'

'Who's afraid?' She tilted her chin defiantly, 'I've been married before, there's nothing to it!' Her mind slipped back and she was in the Register Office—James was a hazy figure—she could hardly see him at all but she could remember the bronze silk dress she'd worn and the cool orchid pinned to it. She hadn't felt as bad then as she did now, but then her life had been simple and uncomplicated—she'd been marrying a simple and uncomplicated man, a man she could understand. Not like now, when she wasn't understanding anything. 'Nothing to it at all!' She repeated it stoutly, more to convince herself than him.

'So, everything is well and you'll drive up tomorrow,' he nodded. 'I'll attend to the hotel bill before I leave and please, don't insult me by offering your share.'

'Humph!' She became sarcastic as she poured more lemon juice on to the ice in her glass and stirred it all up with the long-handled spoon. 'There's little chance of me insulting you by doing that—I couldn't afford a place like this—as a matter of fact,' she rummaged in her bag and produced her purse, counting the notes carefully, 'I've about enough to buy a few little gifts and pay for my petrol—that's in cash and,' she flared as he smiled and reached into his pocket, 'don't you dare offer me money! That would be insulting me!'

'I wasn't going to,' he answered her mildly. 'I was merely going to give you the telephone number of the villa in case you ran out of petrol and money on the way there. *Cara*, what's the matter with you? You're as nervous as a cat.'

'You know very well what's wrong,' she grumbled, holding her glass firmly in both hands so that the chill of the ice cooled down her fingers and stopped them trembling.

'Yes, I think I do,' he gave her his beautiful smile, 'and much as I want to, *cara*, I can't do anything about it yet.'

'No, it's not that!' Under his gaze, the blood rushed to her cheeks.

'Yes it is, Claudia.' His finger touched her hot cheek in a caress. 'We want but as yet, we can't have. We wait and the waiting grows longer each moment.'

He had half the truth there. If she could have married him this very moment, it would be settled and done—no more worrying, no more thoughts of escape. This was worse than waiting for her own execution.

At four o'clock, she stood waving as the Chevrolet rolled silently away from the hotel and when it was out of sight, she went back to the suite and looked around. Without Nico and his mother, it looked very big and lonely and although it was hers until the next morning, she didn't want to stay in it, not another minute. Swiftly, she packed her things into her small case, pushing the overflow into a couple of plastic bags—she'd take a bet it was the first time a guest had ever left these exalted surroundings with luggage in carrier bags— and went to where the Allegro was parked.

Flinging her stuff into the back seat, she gently eased the little car out from between a Lamborghini and a stately Mercedes, taking great care not to scratch either of these high-born vehicles as she did so and at the last moment, with a grunt of pure disgust at her forgetfulness, she remembered about the keys of the suite which were in her bag. She didn't wish to come back here!

The keys returned to the reception desk, she drove away with a feeling of elation tinged with sadness and an hour and several wrong turns later, she drew up outside Maris' apartment. All she needed was bread and butter which she'd bought and she made herself comfortable amid all the black and white cubes. There was plenty of stuff in the larder and cupboards but she couldn't eat—her appetite had vanished so she made a pot of coffee. It tasted rather strange but only because it wasn't fresh coffee and she'd forgotten about needing milk and after a shower, she went to bed, wrinkling her nose as she slid between the black silk of the sheets—and then slithering out from between them to lie on top and cover herself with the embroidered spread.

The Allegro was safely hidden away in a tiny car park at the back of the building, out of sight from the street—the car itself was undistinguished, it wouldn't attract a second glance, but the British number plate was a dead give away. But what was she bothering about? Nobody would come looking for her—this was her lonely time—what she'd wanted, thought she needed and now she had it, she didn't want it any more. She wanted Nico, wanted him until the wanting was an actual physical pain.

Claudia woke late in the morning, feeling utterly unrefreshed and even a cool shower did little to help her feel any better. She had slept but her dreams had been too disturbing for the sleep to have done her any good. Oddly enough, she couldn't recall anything about the dreams except that they'd contained Nico and hadn't been happy. Covered with a towelling robe she'd found behind the bathroom door, she pattered about the apartment in her bare feet for a while, chewing at a buttered crust and taking sips—which made her shudder—from a cup of the almost tasteless coffee and then, dressed in a pair of pink slacks which she'd bought under the direction of the signora, and a shirt of slightly darker pink, she made her way to the bar on the corner of the street.

Here, she bought milk and a ticket at the cash desk, going then to stand at the counter to eat a large chunk of pizza and washing it down with a decent cup of coffee. The pizza was very satisfying and extremely cheap, she decided to repeat the performance this evening before she left for the villa—perhaps sit at one of the few tables instead of standing at the bar but—she watched what went on closely—the service wasn't as quick at the tables, one had to sit around waiting to be served.

When she got back to the apartment, she put the carton of milk in the fridge, which seemed to be working quite well after its two-year rest—and left the coffee, still in its wrappings, on the counter while she fetched a biro and a piece of paper from her bag to make a list of things she had to do. Throw away all the tinned foods and packaged goods for a start—she'd noticed that two of the tins had blown—it might be dangerous to leave them around—and then she had to see about getting Maris' jewel box to Signor Marinotta.

She had meant to attend to that yesterday but the signora's obvious frailty and Nico's arrival had driven it from her mind, it was only the heaviness of her shoulder bag which had reminded her and now, it was too late to catch the *avvocat*, he didn't go to his office at weekends. Registered post—if the box wasn't too heavy—*raccomandata*, was that the word? This sent her hunting through her phrase book because, although she thought she'd remembered it correctly, it didn't sound right to her ears.

She put the box on a low table and, on impulse, added her engagement ring together with the pearl and turquoise one which Nico's mother had given her—not that she had any intention of parting with them, she just wanted to see what it felt like to be free again. But there was no feeling of freedom and the diamond winked accusingly at her as the sunlight caught every one of its rose-cut facets. When Nico had first given it to her, she'd disliked it—a vulgar display of wealth—but now it exerted a certain attraction and her finger felt naked without it. But her finger would have to stay naked for a while at least, she had work to do.

There were a couple of cardboard cartons stacked in the small larder, which she took into the bedroom and stood them by the wardrobe to await filling and hurried back to the kitchen to deal with the tins, bottles and jars. The waste bin was empty and, methodically, she filled it—two years was too long to keep tinned food, especially in this heat— she wasn't sure about pasta and spices but it was better to take no chances so they followed the tins into the bin and when everything was cleared away, she wiped down the shelves.

It was very quiet in the apartment, the windows were triple glazed against the traffic noise from the busy Corso so Claudia's head jerked up in alarm when she heard a soft movement in the hallway. The cleaning woman or another intruder? Her hand went to the pocket of her pink slacks but the keyring wasn't in it—she must have left it in the door when she came back from the bar.

Through the open door of the kitchen, she saw

him, a him, not the woman cleaner, and then, with a sigh of relief, she recognised Sandro; for a moment, she'd been quite frightened. But what a change from the Sandro she'd met at the villa! Gone was the snappy dressing, the waisted jacket, the knife-edge creased trousers, the silk shirts and the two-tone shoes. Sandro now looked just like any other motorbike enthusiast, a top quality enthusiast, a sort of superior Hell's Angel in his black leathers, heavy looking, long boots which could move so quietly and the personality destroying safety helmet with its darkened visor. But of course she knew him, she was an artist, she had an eye for things like that. She didn't have to see a face to put a name to a figure—the walk, the way the head was carried. . . .

'Sandro?' she called and the figure halted where the hallway bulged into a large square with the doors to the bedroom and bathroom leading off. The square was tiled and furnished like the *salotto* so that with the *salotto* doors wide open, it could be used as an extension of the room to give more space for parties. 'I know you,' she chuckled triumphantly, 'so you can come out from behind that weird helmet. I'm just making some coffee; would you like a cup?' And without giving him a chance to answer, 'I thought you were in Florence—how did you know I was here?'

'A lucky guess—a series of lucky guesses.' He emerged from the helmet without disturbing one glossy wave of his black hair and followed her into the kitchen.

Claudia was feeling rather pleased—the afternoon had been looming ahead of her and now that she'd nearly finished what she'd set out to do, she had little to occupy the time which was hanging heavily on her hands—only think about the future and she didn't want to do that. There was nothing to read except some out-of-date fashion magazines in a rack in the *salotto* so any company was welcome as long as whoever it was spoke English, and Sandro did that beautifully.

'I didn't stay long in Firenze.' He followed her back into the kitchen, smiling a rather tight smile. 'I don't like it there. On my mother's side, I'm a Roman and for me, there is only one place to be—in Rome. Here, I'm in the middle of everything; I know everybody; I hear all the gossip—one really lives in Rome. And the gossip,' he smiled secretively, 'that can be very helpful. Within a few hours of your arrival, I knew that you and Nonna Venetia were here in Rome, shopping for your trousseau—I also heard later that my zio had come to join you and then, that he'd taken Nonna back to the villa, leaving you here. I phoned the hotel to ask you to have dinner with me and they told me you'd left so I asked myself where you could have gone. That was where the lucky guesses came in useful. You would have come here to Maris' apartment so that you could search undisturbed.'

He sat down on one of the kitchen chairs and leaned back with an almost triumphant smile curving his mouth. 'I even know what you're searching for,' he added.

Claudia found herself regretting her enthusiastic welcome. Not only did Sandro look different, he was behaving differently, slyly and with an air of exultant—she searched for the right word but could only come up with 'menace', although she thought that was a bit too strong. But he was certainly behaving oddly.

A vague unease gripped her, and she tried to conceal it by calmly walking to and fro between the table and the counter, bringing cups and saucers, opening the fresh carton of milk and the new packet of coffee and being meticulous about the quantity of coffee she spooned into the filter machine.

'You knew Maris?' She made it almost an idle question. 'What made you connect me with her?'

He took the questions in order. 'Yes, I knew Maris—we had a business arrangement,' he made a vague, sweeping gesture at the window, a gesture which emcompassed the city roaring away outside. 'Everybody knows me, you see—at least, anybody who is anybody knows me—I'm very fashionable—I always get invitations to the best parties. Maris wished to design and make clothes for people like my friends, the cream of Roman society she wished to—er—move up in the world of fashion. I helped her, I took her to the parties and places where she could meet the aristocracy, the exclusive people,' he gave her an innocently smug smile. 'As I said, I always have invitations to that sort of thing—my mother's family, you know; she was a contessa in her own right—a member of one of Rome's oldest and greatest families. I introduced Maris to people she'd never have met without my help.'

'But I bet she never mentioned me,' Claudia prodded, still uneasy but determined not to show it. To her mind, Sandro seemed to have a very 'off' set of values. He appeared to think nobody was worth knowing if they didn't have a handle to their name. She could understand Maris' attitude— her cousin had always been ambitious—she'd had talent and she knew it—she'd been determined to get to the top of her profession and she would have used anybody and anything to achieve that objective. One could gain a lot of kudos from designing for a princess and kudos was what counted in the rag trade—it sold clothes at fancy prices and spattered a designer's name across the daily papers.

'She only mentioned you once,' Sandro interrupted her thoughts. 'But I've a very good memory, I never forget anything. We were at a party and a woman there, one of the guests, was wearing something Maris said was fabulous. She told me she wished she had you by her side because you could have done a quick sketch and she could have had the identical thing in her boutique within twenty-four hours.'

'But I still don't see. . . .' She worried her face into a frown.

'How I connected you?' He gave her a self-congratulatory smile. 'Because I'm clever, of course! I'd heard about the woman staying at the Villa Cristal—that you were an artist so I came to see for myself and I was right. There's a definite resemblance between you and Maris but even without that, I'd have known. You see, I know my zio Nicolo. He never does anything without a good reason and he wouldn't have engaged himself to you, taken you to live at the big villa, brought his mother across from Venice and made everything so neat and tidy unless he had a use for you.' The mood of self-congratulation vanished to be replaced by one of self-pitying waspishness. 'My zio has everything and he still isn't satisfied. He wants the little I have—he wants it all. And you see, I was right again; Maris is dead and everything she had came to you including my things, things I loaned her and which she hadn't returned to me. Where are they, Claudia?' and abruptly, his manner turned to one of silky menace.

'I know they're here somewhere and I mean to have them,' he continued grittily. 'They're mine, you know—even my dear zio admits that.' Back came the self-pity with a rush and Claudia marvelled that his moods could change so quickly. Wasn't that a sign of instability? 'They're all I have left of my inheritance,' he almost whined. 'My zio has the rest; my house, my land, my furnishings, my paintings. He sits in my house, enjoying my possessions, he strides about my lands, turns my estate into a co-operative. Oh yes,' as her mouth opened in protest, 'he paid for them, of course, but a niggardly sum, not even half of their real worth and he was cunning—all Venetians are cunning, you can see it in their foxy eyes—it was he who influenced my father so that all the money was put into a trust fund—he made sure I'd never be able to touch it except for a paltry allowance, a pittance I receive each month.'

Claudia rose quickly and crossed to the counter where the coffee machine was issuing clouds of steam and burping ominously. Her feelings of unease had crystallised into nothing less than fear but she knew she had to be calm and conceal it.

'I don't know what you're talking about.' The steadiness of her voice surprised her—she had expected it to wobble. 'Honestly Sandro,' she made it as firm and convincing as she knew how. 'I just don't understand what all this is about, what you're talking about. I'm only sure of one thing and that is that there's nothing here which belongs to you.'

'There is!' Had he been twenty years younger, she thought he would have stamped in sheer, childish frustration. 'My things have to be here, Maris wouldn't have kept them anywhere else. . . .'

'Her *avvocato*. . . .' she suggested desperately because she couldn't think of anything else.

'Oh no,' he wagged his head at her wisely. 'She wouldn't have dared do that. I'm talking about my mother's jewellery—her emeralds—the things neither my father nor Zio could keep from me. They couldn't be sold, they belonged to my mother, not my father, and they're famous— everybody knows about my mother's emeralds so Maris wouldn't have taken them to that stupid old man, he'd have recognised them, asked her how she came to have them. Besides, I told her it had to be a secret and Maris was good at secrets.'

'Then that rules out the *avvocato*.' Claudia sought inspiration from the ceiling. 'Perhaps the bank—a safety deposit box?'

'No!' This time Sandro thumped the table as though he was being driven by her stupidity to lose control of himself. 'I tell you, no! They're here, in this apartment. It's what she said she'd done with them when I told her how valuable they were and how she mustn't let anybody know she had them She laughed at me, me!'

'Was it you who broke in here before?'

'Yes.' He seemed rather proud of the fact. 'Only both times, I was disturbed before I could make a thorough search, the first time it was the man downstairs and last time—I was getting a bit desperate, you see—it was the cleaner.' He gave a pleased, excited, high-pitched giggle. 'I was here when she came but she ran off, yelling about the broken locks, so I had plenty of time to get away.

But I didn't even find Maris' jewel box although I know it must be here somewhere. Maris was always good at hiding things.'

'Her jewel box.' Claudia heard the relief in her own voice—she now had an excuse to get out of the kitchen, maybe, if she was lucky, out of the apartment. She couldn't ring anybody—there was nobody to ring and in any case, the phone had been disconnected two years ago. And what could she say except that her *fidanzato's* nephew had walked in through an open door? The police would laugh at her!

Her thoughts took less than a second before she continued calmly. 'I found the jewel box, Sandro, but I knew where to look for it. I expect what you want's in there. Wait a moment and I'll get it for you.' But when she attempted to pass him to get out of the kitchen, he caught her arm in a bruising grip, stopping her in her tracks.

'Oh no, Claudia, we'll go together. I don't trust you.'

'All right,' she tried to sound disinterested. 'The box is on a coffee table in the *salotto*, you can't miss it. Go and see for yourself.'

'We'll go together.' He gave her an unpleasant smile. 'I said I don't trust you. You've found my things and you must have known they were mine but you didn't say a word. You were going to keep them for yourself, I know! I'm not a fool so don't try to treat me like one!'

No, not a fool, she agreed with him silently—as mad as a hatter that was all! She was mewed up in this apartment with a lunatic and nobody knew she was here—one had to humour lunatics, they could be dangerous and at the back of her mind, she was frightened. 'Come along then.' She tried to

prise his fingers from her arm but met with no
success. 'Let's go and have a look. Perhaps I've
found what you're looking for.' The smile he gave
her nearly convinced her of his craziness, it was
bright, glittering and full of a queer satisfaction as
she winced when his fingers tightened even harder
about her arm.

'Now you're being sensible, Claudia,' even his
voice was different, high and shaking with
excitement. 'If you hadn't told me, if you'd made
me search for them myself, I was going to hurt
you. I could, you know, easily—I'm very strong.'

'There's no need for violence,' she controlled the
quiver of fright in her voice. 'I don't want your
things, Sandro. . . .'

'But my zio does.' Once again he tightened his
hand and tears of pain filled her eyes. 'My zio
wants everything. It's Nonna Venetia really, she's
behind it all. She always hated my father because
he was the elder son—she couldn't live in the villa,
you know, she made my nonno go and live with
her in Venice. Even then, she wanted everything
for Zio Nicolo—she still does. She calls it "mother
love" but it's really greed and envy because my
mother's family was patrician. Nonna Venetia isn't
noble like them although she's learned to act like a
great lady—her family were artisans, plebs—they
were in trade. They have a factory,' he gave a
shudder of revulsion. 'They make glass for the
tourist trade!'

'How low can you get,' Claudia murmured it
sympathetically as they walked towards the coffee
table where she'd dumped the jewel box, ready for
packaging. Without releasing her, Sandro reached
covetously for the silver box which was lying
directly beneath the hooves of a prancing glass

stallion. She kept her eyes on it, a lovely thing in creamy translucent glass, beautifully modelled with a matt surface and the mane and flowing tail added in glossy white.

'You need two hands to open it,' she continued conversationally although she could feel her tongue dry and too big for her mouth. 'And you needn't be afraid I'll run away. If what you want is in that box, you're welcome to it. As you said, it's yours, not mine.'

Sandro released her arm to fiddle with the catch and she stood quietly, watching and waiting for her chance. It would have to be the bathroom, there was a substantial bolt on the inside of the door. She'd lock herself in, open the window and scream her head off. . . .

The box flew open and in his excitement, Sandro lost his grip on it so that it fell to the floor, scattering pearls, gold chains, rings, brooches and earrings all over the carpet, but before he dropped on his knees to scrabble amid the pile, he turned on her like a vexed child.

'That was *your* fault,' he almost yelled and swung his arm so that the flat of his palm caught her a blow across the face and then, as if she no longer existed for him, he was down on all fours, searching.

Claudia rocked on her heels, regained her balance and picked up the glass stallion. Her last thought as she hit him with it was that she hoped it wasn't *very* valuable.

CHAPTER TEN

CLAUDIA stood, looking down at Sandro's body, for what seemed a long time and then, with a little moan of despair, she sank into a chair and put her head down between her knees. The stallion statuette still dangled from her hand, right in front of her eyes—she didn't seem able to let it go and she whimpered with revulsion at what she'd done. Such a small thing, for despite its weight—and it was heavy—it was quite small. Her eyes slid to the still figure on the carpet and away again swiftly. He hadn't moved and he was very quiet—did people become that still and quiet when they were merely unconscious, or had she killed him!

The idea took root in her mind, grew swiftly and blossomed into a hideous conviction. He was dead and there would be a scandal. It would be in all the papers—Nico would kill her! 'Man beaten to death in Rome apartment—British artist claims self defence!' Her mind ran on sluggishly. Perhaps he wasn't dead, she ought to do something—a cold compress on the back of his neck, take his pulse, but when she tried to move, her legs wouldn't hold her and she sat down again swiftly, trying hard not to look at the black-leather-clad figure.

Maris would have approved of that, she heard herself giggle hysterically—black leather—he went with the decor—and now, she couldn't stop looking at him, no matter how hard she tried to turn her head away. The soles of the strong-looking boots were of rubber, heavily cleated—no

wonder he'd been able to move about so quietly—
if only he would move now! Any small movement,
a faint groan would do.

She heard the click of the main door closing and
raised frightened eyes to see Nico coming across
the floor towards her. He should have been at the
villa with his mother but his being here didn't
surprise her, not a bit. She didn't think she'd ever
be surprised again.

'Come in,' she croaked from a dry throat and
then, wearily, 'Everybody come in. This is an open
house, no need to knock. Just walk in! He walked
in,' she made a small gesture with her free hand at
Sandro but she kept her eyes riveted on Nico's
face, watching the expressions flit across it, trying
to sort them out. Quick anger and as quickly
gone—surprise, or had she been mistaken? Nothing
ever seemed to surprise him! She watched him
drop on one knee and probe among Sandro's
glossy black waves of hair. 'I've killed him, I
think,' she announced.

'Not this time,' Nico straightened up and
reached for her hand, the one still holding the
glass horse, and he removed it gently from her
fingers, prising each one from where shock had
glued them to the smooth, almost satiny surface.

'You mean he's still alive?' Reaction had set in
and she was beginning to shiver uncontrollably.

'Mmm,' he stirred Sandro's prone body with his
foot and she heard a faint groan, she thought it
was the most beautiful sound she'd ever heard in
her life. 'But he's going to have a very bad
headache when he wakes up.' Nico drew her to her
feet and when she sagged at the knees, he picked
her up and carried her into the kitchen. 'Nothing
worse than a headache, *cara*, I promise and I hope

it teaches him a lesson. Other than that, you've done no lasting damage, not even to the horse. Could you not have used something a little less beautiful, a rolling pin perhaps? It would have been a pity if you'd broken it—one of our best productions—a limited edition—over subscribed but we made a few more to fill the list.' As he busied himself with emptying and refilling the coffee machine, he went on idly chatting about the horse. 'Not for the tourist trade of course—it was much too expensive—mostly for collectors—an investment because it's a fine piece and quite rare. Your cousin must have had it as a gift, I can't recall her name on the subscription list.'

'D-damn the horse!' Claudia was beginning to feel better. Nico had said she'd done no lasting damage and she was trying hard to believe him but some doubt still remained. 'Shouldn't we go and look at him—call an ambulance or a doctor or something?'

'No!' He was definite. 'We'll let him sleep it off.' His eyes gleamed and a smile curved his mouth and creased his cheek. 'He'll probably wish you had killed him when he wakes up. He's going to rue the day he tangled with my modern-day Boadicea.'

It should have made her feel good—it did make her feel good—her voice strengthened and she regained some animation—enough so that her temper started to rise. She thought of all she'd been through and when Nico pushed a steaming cup of coffee in front of her, she ladled in sugar with a generous hand which still shook.

'He's mad!' Outrage raised her voice to an unusual shrillness. 'Quite mad! Coming here, sneaking in! He's broken in here twice before, you

know. Signor Marinotta is fed up with having the
locks changed because he's broken them. . . .'

'He didn't need to break them this time,' Nico
was stern, almost accusing. 'You left the key
outside the door, in the lock—it was still there
when I arrived.'

'What if I did?' she was nearly herself again and
being belligerent. 'That's no reason for him to just
walk in as though he owned the place. He
frightened me half to death, looking like something
from outer space in that ridiculous safety
helmet. . . .'

'Looking for his emeralds, I suppose,' Nico was
mild, even faintly humorous.

'You know about them?' Surprise raised her
voice to a squeak.

'Of course,' he nodded smugly. 'There must
have been some reason why your cousin thought
he was going to marry her and I can't think of any
other—she wasn't pregnant at the time of the
accident so it couldn't have been that.'

'M-Maris thought *Sandro* was going to marry
her?' Claudia took a gulp of too-hot coffee,
burned her mouth and raised her hand to her lips.
It was one way of keeping them still, the only way
she could think of. Dear god, what had she done—
two years and she'd been wrong all the time—but
Nico seemed not to have noticed anything, he was
still speaking and she listened carefully to make
sense of what she'd missed.

'. . . must have known about his reputation but
some girls never seem to learn.'

'He's got a reputation, has he?' It was better to
go on normally, she could think about the other
later, so she sparkled ominously and watched
Nico's face crease into another smile.

'Not the sort you're thinking about,' he shook his head. 'Sandro's usually very discreet about his "little friends". He dangles his emeralds in front of them until they're dazzled, sometimes he lends them a small piece, but he's always had it back when the affair's over. No, I mean his reputation for being the biggest snob in Rome. He has a fixation about birth and breeding, do you understand?' and when she nodded, remembering Sandro's scathing remarks about Nico's mother, 'I don't think he'd even consider a girl as a worthy wife unless she was at least a contessa. Now me,' his eyes gleamed and he tried to look modest, 'I'm more modern in my thinking. I'm quite prepared to marry an artist of no particular lineage. . . .'

'He's also violent,' she interrupted fiercely. 'Never mind about anything else. He hit me, slapped my face. He ought to be locked up, put in a strait jacket—marched off to the nearest psychiatric ward. Accusing me of having his bits and bobs! I've never laid eyes on the stuff!' For a moment, the actual presence of Sandro was forgotten although she was talking about him. The young man in black leathers and space-age helmet who had invaded her privacy had diminished to be part of a nightmare she was trying to forget— although it flatly refused to be forgotten.

'He hurt you, *cara*?' Nico's hand was very gentle as he lifted her chin and turned her face to the light. She heard the hiss of his breath as his eyes took in the mark on her cheek and in a self-pitying way, she was glad the blow had been hard enough to leave a mark.

'I told you, he slapped my face—hard! That was after he'd threatened to hurt me. He was in a rage because he'd dropped the box and all the stuff scattered on the floor.' She paused and a smile of pure complacency turned her lips up at the corners. 'You should have heard me! A cooing dove had nothing on me! I was all sweet reason and helpfulness. I even offered to help him search. Rather brave of me, don't you think?'

Her mood changed like lightning and she pushed away the finger under her chin with angry hands. 'How did you know I was here?' she demanded angrily. 'He,' she gestured in the direction of the *salotto*, 'he told me how he knew where to find me—he phoned the hotel but he'd already worked out I was a connection of Maris'— something she said about me once—that and a resemblance, although I've never seen it myself. Now it's your turn to make with the explanations. I suppose you've been here before as well. Going on at this rate, there won't have been a personable man in Rome who hasn't been here. Who should I expect next?' But scolding him, almost accusing him, didn't help, her conscience was still pricking.

'I also phoned the hotel, Claudia, but I did that when we arrived at the villa last night. Next time, if you wish to leave an hotel secretly, don't hand the key in to the reception desk and tell them you've finished with it. Leave it on the inside of your door for the maids to find in the morning. You had to sleep somewhere, I didn't think you'd attempt the drive in the dark—I knew about your cousin—the rest followed naturally. . . .'

A muffled thump, the crash of an overturned chair and a pain-filled groan from the *salotto* silenced him and they both watched as Sandro came staggering through the kitchen door to lean against the wall while he groaned some more. He looked very dazed, not seeming to notice his uncle but concentrating his attention on Claudia.

'Bitch!' It was a hoarse mutter. 'You tricked me, you bitch.' He heaved himself away from the wall and staggered across the floor to where she was sitting, muttering threats with every unsteady step.

Claudia cowered, shrinking back in her chair. Even with Nico here, she didn't feel very brave. 'No,' she whispered it and her hand went to her cheek in a protective gesture. Nico interrupted, turning his nephew's attention to himself.

'You've come to apologise for your behaviour, nepito?'

'Dear Zio,' Sandro's face twisted in a travesty of his usual charming smile. 'You expect me to apologise—to her?' The words came out slowly as though he had to think before he said each one. 'Zio, she has my emeralds, she's found them and hidden them from me—she means to keep them for herself—just like her cousin! She wouldn't give them back to me either—she laughed in my face and told me I could have them on our wedding day—and I'd only loaned them to her.'

More confirmation of her mistake. Claudia's face whitened. She wanted to get to her feet and yell, 'But I didn't know it was you!' and only Nico's voice, cold and hard, stopped her.

'Sandro, you've been very fortunate so far. Claudia hasn't sent for the police and if you apologise to her for your abominable behaviour, I might be able to talk her out of charging you with assault.'

'You say I assaulted her?' Sandro slumped into a chair, holding his head in his hands. 'Zio! Can't you see what she did to me?'

Nico's laugh was soft and mocking. 'Sandro, don't be foolish. How could a frail woman have injured you so—a frail, frightened woman—it would sound ridiculous and the paparazzi would spread it all over their front pages. No, of course, you couldn't tell a story like that, you would be laughed out of Rome. The truth is, you fell and struck your head on something or,' he pondered a moment, 'better still, you skidded on your motorbike, hit your head and, feeling ill while close to this apartment, you sought the help of my *fidanzata*, who you knew was staying here while she completed the shopping for her trousseau. Yes,' he looked at his nephew meditatively, 'I think that is the story you will tell—and Claudia, expecting me hourly, decided to wait a while before she sent for a doctor or an ambulance—she was worried in case your accident had involved another vehicle or a pedestrian. That is what you will tell everybody, isn't it, Sandro?' A child would have understood the implied threat and one look at Nico's face, rock hard and implacable, was enough, but not for Sandro. He harked back to his trinkets and his voice, now stronger and less slurred, held a note of grievance.

'She has my emeralds and everybody knows they're mine. They're famous! My mother, my grandmother, my great grandmother all wore them. . . .'

'In a direct line back to Messalina and we all know what she was like!' Claudia forgot about her conscience for a moment as she murmured *soto voce* and with malice to be rewarded by a haughty glare from her *fidanzato* who was elaborating on the fictitious accident.

'Your motorbike skidded, Sandro, but fortunately the street was completely empty, there were no other casualties. I shall phone for a doctor and that is the story you will tell him.'

'And meanwhile, you will enjoy my emeralds. . . .'

'My dear nephew,' Nico sounded insufferable,
and Claudia silently cheered him on. 'I dislike
emeralds and my *fidanzata* shares my distaste for
them, so, don't mention them again.'

'You can't phone from here,' Claudia pointed
out. 'It's been disconnected for a couple of years.'

Nico rewarded her with a smile. 'You see,
Sandro, another reason why Claudia couldn't get
you immediate attention, no phone in the
apartment and she felt unable to leave you—she
didn't know how badly you'd been injured.'

Sandro made to rise, thought better of it and sat
down again with a thump—there was an expression
of mulish obstinacy on his handsome face. 'I won't
go without my emeralds—they're here somewhere—they *must* be and without those earrings,
the whole set is spoiled. No! I shall stay here until
they're found!'

'Earrings!' Claudia exploded into wrath. 'All
this fuss about some earrings! I thought it was a
tiara at the very least. You come here, upsetting
everybody about a pair of earrings—smacking my
face. . . .' She wasn't going to forget that blow in a
hurry. 'You've seen every last little bit of valuable
stuff Maris had—you threw it all over the floor,
remember?'

'Maris had other, less valuable things?' That was
Nico being thorough as ever and Claudia eyed him
glassily.

'Most women have junk stuff,' she said crossly.
'You know what I mean—big things to wear for
effect. Maris kept it separate in an old cigar box—
I'll show you, you can see for yourself.' She
marched out of the kitchen to the bedroom,

scrabbled with the spring of the secret drawer and came back with the box, nearly throwing it on the table. 'I've been through it, although I didn't have to. Maris would never have kept anything valuable in that, it isn't even lined besides, most of the things are either old and worn or broken, I was going to throw it all away before I left.'

'Junk stuff!' Nico raised the lid and stirred the contents with a long finger and then he chuckled. '*Cara*, you're too innocent for words to describe. You call these junk?' and he lifted out some green earrings, swinging them gently in one hand while with the other, he fended off his nephew's convulsive grab.

'Those!' Claudia almost sneered at his ignorance. 'A lot *you* know about jewellery! A babe in arms could see they're not worth much. The stones are too big ever to be genuine and the gold plating's worn off so that the copper metal's showing through—besides, they're ugly. They might have looked impressive when they were new and had a bit of a sparkle. . . .'

Nico shook his head sadly. 'You're right about them being old, *cara*, but when these were made, nobody knew about sparkle—it was the size and colour of the stones which was important and as for the worn setting, red gold always looks like that.'

Claudia's eyes went wide and agonised. 'You-you mean they're—and I was going to put them in the waste bin. . . .' She looked across at Sandro and had all the confirmation she needed. He was staring at the earrings as though they were his variation of the Holy Grail—he was almost drooling.

'I told you, Zio! I said she had them! Trying to

steal them and now, when she's caught, daring to say she didn't know—she's lying. . . .'

Claudia's face whitened with fury so that the mark of Sandro's blow stood out on her colourless cheek, a large darkened patch.

'No, I am not!' she shouted him down. 'How *dare* you say that!' She appealed to Nico. 'Believe me please, I didn't know and Maris couldn't have thought much of them either or she wouldn't have tossed them in a box with all the other worthless stuff.'

'Of course, I believe you.' Nico's smile was balm to her wounded spirit. It did look bad, she admitted to herself but if Nico believed that was all that mattered. 'Sandro,' he'd turned his attention to his nephew who was still shouting accusations. 'Be quiet! You heard what Claudia said and you will apologise. . . .'

'No need!' Claudia became haughty. 'I don't care a fig for what he says. As if I'd want his old earrings, I wouldn't be seen dead in them!'

'Which is what I told him a little while ago only I was more polite, *cara*. Now, let's get down to business. First, I shall take Sandro to the hospital—I'll take the door key with me so that, while I'm gone, you will be quite safe from intruders and when I return, you must be ready. I'll take you out for a meal.'

Sandro moaned every step of the way to the door and when it closed behind him and Nico, Claudia trailed off to the bathroom. Her head was aching, she felt as though she'd been beaten half to death and she was swimming in a pool of guilt— no, not swimming, drowning! She'd wasted two years of her life being vengeful towards the wrong man—she could have hurt him, ruined his life.

And he'd have to be told, even if he killed her for it. She'd explain as best she could, he might understand—she'd apologise. She stepped under the shower but there wasn't enough hot water in the world to wash away her feeling of guilt. She towelled herself dry and shrugged into the towelling robe to wander back to the bedroom.

Nico might understand but she couldn't see him being very forgiving, which meant she'd be out! A small piece taken off his personal chess board— not to be played with any more. Shivering, she slumped on the bed, pulled the spread over her and cried herself to sleep.

When she woke, the setting sun was bathing the sky in a rosy glow and gilding the crosses on the twin cupolas of Trinita dei Monte, so that they shone like fire against the evening blue of the sky. There were sounds coming from the kitchen— Nico must be back. She was just slipping from the bed when he tapped at the door and came in with a cup of coffee. Claudia thought it might be better to fight than huddle in misery and came out with a thought which had just struck her.

'Sandro's bike.' She took the cup from his hand, being very careful their fingers didn't touch—any physical contact would make a coward of her and she'd live with guilt for the rest of her days. 'If you said what you said you were going to say—about him skidding—oughtn't the bike to be a bit damaged? It couldn't have survived a crash without a few scratches.'

'It didn't—and I didn't forget,' he looked tired and she had an almost overwhelming desire to pull him down beside her, hold his head against her breast and lull him to sleep. Instead, she curled her legs beneath her and pulled the spread up to cover

them before she fumbled with the belt of the robe,
tightening it.

'Why did you come back to Rome?' she peered
into her cup to avoid looking at him and all the
while, in the back of her mind, she was rehearsing
her explanations and her apology.

'To discover what game you were playing this
time, *amorosa mia*.' He seated himself on the side
of the bed and his mouth curved in its old,
beautiful smile. 'You were being just a little too
reasonable for a woman, I thought—so many
explanations, so many excuses—it isn't like you—
you even spoke about money to prove your point.
About the bike though. I was very careful to run
into it as I drove Sandro out of the car park. You
could have heard his cry of anguish several streets
away. . . .'

'But your car!'

'Undamaged,' he smiled reminiscently. 'I told
you, *cara*, it's a good car. I didn't even dent the
bumper, but Sandro's bike will never be the same
again.'

'And Sandro?' she was seizing on anything to
delay, to keep him by her side.

'Sandro has a very thick skull, or so the X-ray
discloses. Like my car, it wasn't even dented, but
the blow to his head is nothing compared with the
blow to his pride, he's going to hate you for the
rest of his life but it won't matter. We shan't be
seeing much of him in the future.'

'Mmm,' there was a long pause while she fiddled
with the spoon, the handle of the cup and tucked
the spread more firmly about her while she
thought of something to say and Nico wasn't
helping. He was just sitting there, looking at her.
'Y-you said I'd be safe in the hotel.' Try as she

would, she couldn't raise a scrap of fight, her voice was flat with resignation. This was nearly the end, she had only to say a few words but she wanted a few minutes before she told him about her mistake—after that, it would all be over. She'd drive away, out of his life, and if there wouldn't be much to look forward to, or to look back on, she'd get used to it in time.

'Claudia.' He brought her out of her daydream. 'I was trying to warn you about Sandro. I tried before but you didn't seem to listen. I told you, you were playing a dangerous game—all those vengeful thoughts in your head—Sandro can be unpleasant— he's a bit. . . .'

'Mad as a hatter's what you mean,' she managed a small spurt of energy. 'Like the rest of the family—all candidates for the nearest asylum. . . .'

'Nothing of the kind.' He pushed her knees aside and made himself more comfortable. 'There's nothing wrong with the Gabriellis, we're all perfectly normal. . . .'

'You could have fooled me!' She nodded emphatically and then stopped as a pain shot through her temple. 'Sandro getting hot and bothered about some grubby earrings, breaking in to find them, assaulting me, accusing me of wanting to steal them and—but you don't know the best, do you? He actually believed you were marrying me because you wanted them and you thought I had them—how much madder can you get than that! And then, there's you,' she continued, getting into her stride. 'Asking me, a complete stranger— no, telling me I was to marry you and expecting me to obey as if I was a well-trained dog—I don't think that says much for your normality.'

'Claudia.' He seized her arms, pulling her round to face him, his hands almost as painful as Sandro's had been, but this time, she welcomed the pain. 'My nephew's little peculiarities have nothing to do with the Gabriellis—his mother was unstable—too much inbreeding to keep the line pure, I suppose. She had moods of deep depression when she tried to kill herself and soon after Sandro was born, she succeeded. That was why my brother and I concocted our little scheme—Sandro had bouts of unnatural anger as a child, and my brother was worried. I was given the chance to buy everything and the money was put into a fund for the boy, a lifetime fund. . . .'

'Oh dear,' she heaved a sigh and refused to look at him, staring instead at a point just above and behind his shoulder. 'I'm sorry I brought that up, I wasn't trying to delve but you're wrong about one thing so I'd better tell the truth although you're not going to like it very much.' She lowered her gaze and fixed it on the top pocket of his jacket. 'I didn't come here intending to hurt Sandro, you know. How could I? I didn't even know he existed. I didn't know about Maris and Sandro—I thought it was Maris and you!'

'Me!' He raised his eyebrows and beneath them, the dark brown, slanting eyes widened. '*Cara*, how could you have thought that?'

'Why not?' she asked drearily. 'It all added up at the time. Put yourself in my place and see if it didn't. She'd driven us miles out of our way to see this man who was her lover—the man she was going to marry and she hadn't given him a name. It was all hes. "He's the most marvellous man in the world—he's the man I've been looking for all my life—he's the perfect lover and you'll understand as soon as you meet him." Then I saw you and I thought I understood but you were angry, vile to her and brutal. I know I didn't understand what you said to her, you and she were both speaking Italian, but rejection's the same in any language, it's a visible thing. I saw her break up, she literally went to pieces right in front of my eyes and afterwards, when she came round a bit, she was hysterical with rage and hate.' There was a wry twist to her mouth as she added, 'Maris wasn't used to rejection and I suppose that's how the accident happened—she wasn't fit to drive but she wouldn't let me or James so I blamed you for everything. I thought there was a debt to pay. Maris and James were dead but I was alive, so. . . .'

'James meant so much to you?' She blinked with surprise. It wasn't what she'd expected him to say, she'd been prepared for icy contempt, blistering rage but this quiet question, that she hadn't been prepared for and she struggled for honesty.

'Then, yes. All the plans we'd made—the future, my future, had James in it and suddenly, he was gone. I hated you for what you'd done, I told myself there were other, kinder ways you could have broken it off with her—that you must be the hardest, most self-centred man I'd ever met—that you hadn't an ounce of human pity and you didn't know the meaning of mercy—so, you didn't deserve any pity or mercy shown to you. You'd had what you wanted, only now, I know it wasn't you. . . .'

'I'll admit to being very angry that night,' Nico echoed her wry smile as he took her hand from where her fingers were tracing patterns on the spread. 'Too angry, I'm afraid. I'd been disturbed in the middle of a well-earned dinner by a distraught young woman seeking her lover. I wasn't feeling hospitable because this wasn't the first time it had happened—there had been others. Sandro usually left me with the task of getting rid of his women when he'd grown tired of them or when they became too pressing. But surely, your cousin must have described him,' he rumpled his guinea-gold hair. 'Nobody could ever mistake me for my nephew.'

'No,' she shook her head lethargically. 'No description. "Wonderful", "Marvellous", "Heavenly", that's all and afterwards, when I left the hospital in Rome—when Signor Marinotta told me about the boutique, the apartment and the little villa, he mentioned your name—he even described you, so I put two and two together and made five. I'm sorry. I was wrong but I didn't know it.'

There, it was all said and all she wanted was a dark, deep hole to crawl into but wasn't there one last thing? Yes and she wasn't going to finish on a defeatist note. 'I came to Italy to hurt you, if I could. I was still going to hurt you, right up until yesterday.' A fugitive colour swept into her cheeks and drained away swiftly, leaving her pale but composed. 'I knew you wanted me so I played you along. I was going to run out on you—I never meant to marry you. I let you make all the plans and I was going to leave. . . .'

'But you love me, *cara*.' His hand tightened on hers. 'No, don't shake your head. You've said you knew I wanted you—I also knew you wanted me. Yes, you did and you still do!'

'Oh,' she tried to be sophisticated about it. 'You mean the physical thing, but don't you see? Once that's been fed, it'll die—that's why I offered—to get it out of my system so I wouldn't think about it or you any more.'

Nico grabbed for her and pulled her close so that, beneath her cheek, she could hear the thud of his heart beat. 'You and your offers!' She could hear the smile in his voice. 'So that's why you made it—*idiota!* The only way that "thing" might die is for it to be undernourished; properly fed, it will last us the rest of our lives. There's more to it than mere carnality, *carissima.* I loved you, it was sudden and unexpected but I accepted it—I also knew you needed time, not just to forget but to learn to live again, to love again and,' he put his hand in his pocket, took it out and jingled something in his closed palm, 'you've done what you set out to do, *cara*; you've rejected me.' He opened his hand to show the two rings lying there. 'Now your revenge is complete, you threw my rings on the floor!'

'I didn't,' she protested. 'I only took them off for a little while. Sandro must have knocked them off the table, I wasn't thinking about revenge, not then.'

She watched, hypnotised, as he replaced the ring which had been his mother's gift, first sliding her wedding ring from her right hand before he slid the pearl and turquoise ring into place on her third finger. For a moment, he weighed the plain gold circle in his hand, his face expressionless and her heart gave a lurch as their eyes met.

'Can you put this away now, *cara?*' He was rather sombre.

'Yes.' She was equally grave and watched as he laid the ring down quietly on the bedside table. There was an air of finality about the click as it touched the black glass surface—like the click of a door being closed quietly but firmly.

'And this?' He was back to his old mockery as he held out the extravagant diamond. 'I don't think you ever truly liked it. . . .'

Claudia took her courage in both hands and held out her left. 'It's something that grows on you.' It was a watery little joke, there were tears in her eyes and her voice shook a little. 'I was beginning to think it wasn't so flashy after all, more sort of solid and dependable—like your car.' The ring slid home and she gulped. 'Does this mean. . . .'

'That I love you and I want everybody to know it—you to know it.'

'Mmm,' she dashed away the last tear with the back of her hand, 'but there are other, less expensive ways you could have done that—you could just have said it, I'd have believed you.' She gave him a weak smile, weak because she was still partly unbelieving. 'Your trouble is, you've been mixing with the wrong women.'

'As I've already confessed, a few. *Cara*, we're playing a dangerous game,' as she slid her arms round his neck and hugged herself closer to him, pulling his head down to hers and seeking his mouth with hungry lips.

'Food first and then we must be on our way,' Nico stirred beside her and she opened dreamy bemused eyes to gaze at him. She'd been away, a peak in Darien perhaps, where, against the dark silk of the sky, she'd seen the sun, the moon and all the stars come together in blinding light which had taken her breath away with the beauty of it. He'd been fiercely gentle and savagely tender, and now she was comfortable and she didn't want to move.

'On our way—where?'

'Back to the villa.' He rolled over and looked down at her. 'I have a wedding planned for next Saturday—you are going to attend, I hope! You have a leading role, dressed in cream satin with a spray of—what were they—apricot-coloured roses? It'll be a disaster if you aren't there!'

A tempting offer from Mills & Boon

Temptation is a new kind of romance from Mills & Boon. Exciting, sensuous, compelling... written for today's woman. Two new titles will be published every month, starting in February.

And to make Temptation totally irresistible, the February and March titles can be yours for the special introductory price of just 99p.

Go on – give in to Temptation.

SPECIAL INTRODUCTORY PRICE
ONLY 99P EACH

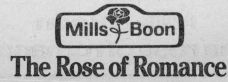

🌹 ROMANCE

Variety is the spice of romance

Each month, Mills & Boon publish new romances. New stories about people falling in love. A world of variety in romance — from the best writers in the romantic world. Choose from these titles in February.

WINTER SUN, SUMMER RAIN Ann Charlton
PRODIGAL SISTER Catherine George
MISS MARY'S DEVIL Emma Goldrick
GOWN OF SCARLET Samantha Harvey
A STRANGER TO LOVE Donna Huxley
THE FRIENDSHIP BARRIER Penny Jordan
THE SCORPIO MAN Claudia Jameson
COMRADE WOLF Madeleine Ker
NO OTHER LOVE Mary Lyons
TEMPESTUOUS AFFAIR Carole Mortimer
THE GABRIELLI MAN Jeneth Murrey
HUNTER'S FORTUNE Nicola West

On sale where you buy paperbacks. If you require further information or have any difficulty obtaining them, write to: Mills & Boon Reader Service, PO Box 236, Thornton Road, Croydon, Surrey CR9 3RU, England.

Mills & Boon
the rose of romance

Give the Rose of Romance on Mother's Day.

DESIRABLE PROPERTY
Catherine George

A SUMMER IDYLL
Betty Neels

THE ONLY ONE
Penny Jordan

NEVER IN A LIFETIME
Lilian Peake

Bring someone some romance this Mother's Day. Four brand new titles from Mills and Boon, attractively gift wrapped for £4.40.
Look for this gift pack where you buy Mills and Boon romances – it's available from 8th February 1985.

Take 4
Exciting Books
Absolutely
FREE

Love, romance, intrigue... all are captured for you by Mills & Boon's top-selling authors. By becoming a regular reader of Mills & Boon's Romances you can enjoy 6 superb new titles every month plus a whole range of special benefits: your very own personal membership card, a free monthly newsletter packed with recipes, competitions, exclusive book offers and a monthly guide to the stars, plus extra bargain offers and big cash savings.

AND an introductory FREE GIFT for YOU.
Turn over the page for details.

As a special introduction we will send you four exciting Mills & Boon Romances Free and without obligation when you complete and return this coupon.

At the same time we will reserve a subscription to Mills & Boon Reader Service for you. Every month, you will receive 6 of the very latest novels by leading Romantic Fiction authors, delivered direct to your door. You don't pay extra for delivery — postage and packing is always completely Free. There is no obligation or commitment — you can cancel your subscription at any time.

You have nothing to lose and a whole world of romance to gain.

Just fill in and post the coupon today to **MILLS & BOON READER SERVICE, FREEPOST, P.O. BOX 236, CROYDON, SURREY CR9 9EL.**

Please Note:- READERS IN SOUTH AFRICA write to Mills & Boon, Postbag X3010, Randburg 2125, S. Africa.

- -

FREE BOOKS CERTIFICATE

To: Mills & Boon Reader Service, FREEPOST, P.O. Box 236, Croydon, Surrey CR9 9EL.

Please send me, free and without obligation, four Mills & Boon Romances, and reserve a Reader Service Subscription for me. If I decide to subscribe I shall, from the beginning of the month following my free parcel of books, receive six new books each month for £6.60, post and packing free. If I decide not to subscribe, I shall write to you within 10 days. The free books are mine to keep in any case. I understand that I may cancel my subscription at any time simply by writing to you. I am over 18 years of age.

Please write in BLOCK CAPITALS.

Signature _____

Name _____

Address _____

_____ Post code _____

SEND NO MONEY — TAKE NO RISKS.

Please don't forget to include your Postcode.

Remember, postcodes speed delivery. Offer applies in UK only and is not valid to present subscribers. Mills & Boon reserve the right to exercise discretion in granting membership. If price changes are necessary you will be notified.

6R   *Offer expires June 30th 1985*

EP